California Standards
Enrichment Workbook

McDougal Littell

World History

Medieval and Early Modern Times

California Consultant

Neal Cates
Long Beach Unified School District
Lakewood, California

McDougal Littell
A DIVISION OF HOUGHTON MIFFLIN COMPANY

ART CREDITS

xx *Study of Hands* (1485), Leonardo da Vinci. Silverpoint. 21.6 cm x 15.2 cm. Royal
Library (RL 12558), Windsor Castle. The Royal Collection. © 2002, Her Majesty Queen
Elizabeth II.

ACKNOWLEDGMENTS

Excerpt from "To Dawn," and "To Night," from *The Rig Veda*, translated by Nicol Macnicol.
Reprinted by permission of Everyman's Library, David Campbell Publishers, Ltd.

Excerpt from *The Koran Interpreted,* translated by Arthur J. Arberry. Reprinted by
permission of HarperCollins Publishers, Ltd.

Excerpt from "Samurai's Instructions to His Son" by Hojo Shigetoki, from *A History of
Japan to 1334,* edited by George Sansom. Copyright © 1958 by Stanford University Press.
Reprinted by permission of the publishers.

History-Social Science Content Standards for California Public Schools reproduced by
permission, California Department of Education, CDE Press, 1430 N Street, Suite 3207,
Sacramento, CA 95814

ISBN 13: 978-0-618-53147-9   ISBN 10: 0-618-53147-5

Printed in the United States of America.

    21 22 0982 15 14 13 12
4500367192

Contents

CA STANDARDS: REPORTING CLUSTER 3: RENAISSANCE/REFORMATION

How to Use This Book

The *California Standards Enrichment Workbook* is yours to mark on, to write in, and to make your own. You can use it in class and take it home. The workbook will help you master social studies curriculum, point by point.

For each specific objective or goal in the Grade 7 California Content Standards, your book contains:

- a **Review** page, to summarize the most important content—the issues, ideas, and people behind important events.

- a **Practice** page, that asks you to recall, interpret, analyze, and apply the historical knowledge.

Complete the pages in the order your teacher assigns them. Your teacher will assign pages that match material in your social studies textbook.

You can use the **Quick Prep** section (pages 1–16) to scan important historic eras, leaders, data, and dates, and to look up and learn key terms. The Quick Prep section serves as a handy reference:

- As you work on Review and Practice pages, you can look up key ideas, dates, and definitions.

- The data can help you make inferences, make connections, or answer your own questions as they arise.

- Before a big test, you might use the Quick Prep to review with a peer, a tutor or family member, or on your own.

California History-Social Science Standards

GRADE 6 History-Social Science Content Standards
Reporting Cluster 1: World History and Geography: Ancient Civilizations

6.1 Students describe what is known through archaeological studies of the early physical and cultural development of humankind from the Paleolithic era to the agricultural revolution.

1. Describe the hunter-gatherer societies, including the development of tools and the use of fire.

2. Identify the locations of human communities that populated the major regions of the world and describe how humans adapted to a variety of environments.

3. Discuss the climatic changes and human modifications of the physical environment that gave rise to the domestication of plants and animals and new sources of clothing and shelter.

6.2 Students analyze the geographic, political, economic, religious, and social structures of the early civilizations of Mesopotamia, Egypt, and Kush.

1. Locate and describe the major river systems and discuss the physical settings that supported permanent settlement and early civilizations.

2. Trace the development of agricultural techniques that permitted the production of economic surplus and the emergence of cities as centers of culture and power.

3. Understand the relationship between religion and the social and political order in Mesopotamia and Egypt.

4. Know the significance of Hammurabi's Code.

5. Discuss the main features of Egyptian art and architecture.

6. Describe the role of Egyptian trade in the eastern Mediterranean and Nile valley.

7. Understand the significance of Queen Hatshepsut and Ramses the Great.

8. Identify the location of the Kush civilization and describe its political, commercial, and cultural relations with Egypt.

9. Trace the evolution of language and its written forms.

6.3 Students analyze the geographic, political, economic, religious, and social structures of the Ancient Hebrews.

1. Describe the origins and significance of Judaism as the first monotheistic religion based on the concept of one God who sets down moral laws for humanity.

2. Identify the sources of the ethical teachings and central beliefs of Judaism (the Hebrew Bible, the Commentaries): belief in God, observance of law, practice of the concepts of righteousness and justice, and importance of study; and describe how the ideas of the Hebrew traditions are reflected in the moral and ethical traditions of Western civilization.

3. Explain the significance of Abraham, Moses, Naomi, Ruth, David, and Yohanan ben Zaccai in the development of the Jewish religion.

4. Discuss the locations of the settlements and movements of Hebrew peoples, including the Exodus and their movement to and from Egypt, and outline the significance of the Exodus to the Jewish and other people.

5. Discuss how Judaism survived and developed despite the continuing dispersion of much of the Jewish population from Jerusalem and the rest of Israel after the destruction of the second Temple in A.D. 70.

6.4 Students analyze the geographic, political, economic, religious, and social structures of the early civilization of Ancient Greece.

1. Discuss the connections between geography and the development of city-states in the region of the Aegean Sea, including patterns of trade and commerce among Greek city-states and within the wider Mediterranean region.

2. Trace the transition from tyranny and oligarchy to early democratic forms of government and back to dictatorship in ancient Greece, including the significance of the invention of the idea of citizenship (e.g., from *Pericles' Funeral Oration*).

3. State the key differences between Athenian, or direct, democracy and representative democracy.

4. Explain the significance of Greek mythology to the everyday life of people in the region and how Greek literature continues to permeate our literature and language today, drawing from Greek mythology and epics, such as Homer's *Iliad* and *Odyssey*, and from *Aesop's Fables*.

5. Outline the founding, expansion, and political organization of the Persian Empire.

6. Compare and contrast life in Athens and Sparta, with emphasis on their roles in the Persian and Peloponnesian Wars.

7. Trace the rise of Alexander the Great and the spread of Greek culture eastward and into Egypt.

8. Describe the enduring contributions of important Greek figures in the arts and sciences (e.g., Hypatia, Socrates, Plato, Aristotle, Euclid, Thucydides).

6.5 **Students analyze the geographic, political, economic, religious, and social structures of the early civilizations of India.**

1. Locate and describe the major river system and discuss the physical setting that supported the rise of this civilization.

2. Discuss the significance of the Aryan invasions.

3. Explain the major beliefs and practices of Brahmanism in India and how they evolved into early Hinduism.

4. Outline the social structure of the caste system.

5. Know the life and moral teachings of Buddha and how Buddhism spread in India, Ceylon, and Central Asia.

6. Describe the growth of the Maurya empire and the political and moral achievements of the emperor Asoka.

7. Discuss important aesthetic and intellectual traditions (e.g., Sanskrit literature, including the *Bhagavad Gita*; medicine; metallurgy; and mathematics, including Hindu-Arabic numerals and the zero).

6.6 **Students analyze the geographic, political, economic, religious, and social structures of the early civilizations of China.**

1. Locate and describe the origins of Chinese civilization in the Huang-He Valley during the Shang Dynasty.

2. Explain the geographic features of China that made governance and the spread of ideas and goods difficult and served to isolate the country from the rest of the world.

3. Know about the life of Confucius and the fundamental teachings of Confucianism and Taoism.

4. Identify the political and cultural problems prevalent in the time of Confucius and how he sought to solve them.

5. List the policies and achievements of the emperor Shi Huangdi in unifying northern China under the Qin Dynasty.

6. Detail the political contributions of the Han Dynasty to the development of the imperial bureaucratic state and the expansion of the empire.

7. Cite the significance of the trans-Eurasian "silk roads" in the period of the Han Dynasty and Roman Empire and their locations.

8. Describe the diffusion of Buddhism northward to China during the Han Dynasty.

6.7 **Students analyze the geographic, political, economic, religious, and social structures during the development of Rome.**

1. Identify the location and describe the rise of the Roman Republic, including the importance of such mythical and historical figures as Aeneas, Romulus and Remus, Cincinnatus, Julius Caesar, and Cicero.

2. Describe the government of the Roman Republic and its significance (e.g., written constitution and tripartite government, checks and balances, civic duty).

3. Identify the location of and the political and geographic reasons for the growth of Roman territories and expansion of the empire, including how the empire fostered economic growth through the use of currency and trade routes.

4. Discuss the influence of Julius Caesar and Augustus in Rome's transition from republic to empire.

5. Trace the migration of Jews around the Mediterranean region and the effects of their conflict with the Romans, including the Romans' restrictions on their right to live in Jerusalem.

6. Note the origins of Christianity in the Jewish Messianic prophecies, the life and teachings of Jesus of Nazareth as described in the New Testament, and the contribution of St. Paul the Apostle to the definition and spread of Christian beliefs (e.g., belief in the Trinity, resurrection, salvation).

6.7 *continued*

7. Describe the circumstances that led to the spread of Christianity in Europe and other Roman territories.

8. Discuss the legacies of Roman art and architecture, technology and science, literature, language, and law.

GRADE 7 History-Social Science Content Standards
Reporting Cluster 2: Late Antiquity and the Middle Ages

7.1 Students analyze the causes and effects of the vast expansion and ultimate disintegration of the Roman Empire.

1. Study the early strengths and lasting contributions of Rome (e.g., significance of Roman citizenship; rights under Roman law; Roman art, architecture, engineering, and philosophy; preservation and transmission of Christianity) and its ultimate internal weaknesses (e.g., rise of autonomous military powers within the empire, undermining of citizenship by the growth of corruption and slavery, lack of education, and distribution of news).

2. Discuss the geographic borders of the empire at its height and the factors that threatened its territorial cohesion.

3. Describe the establishment by Constantine of the new capital in Constantinople and the development of the Byzantine Empire, with an emphasis on the consequences of the development of two distinct European civilizations, Eastern Orthodox and Roman Catholic, and their two distinct views on church-state relations.

7.2 Students analyze the geographic, political, economic, religious, and social structures of the civilizations of Islam in the Middle Ages.

1. Identify the physical features and describe the climate of the Arabian peninsula, its relationship to surrounding bodies of land and water, and nomadic and sedentary ways of life.

2. Trace the origins of Islam and the life and teachings of Muhammad, including Islamic teachings on the connection with Judaism and Christianity.

3. Explain the significance of the Qur'an and the Sunnah as the primary sources of Islamic beliefs, practice, and law, and their influence in Muslims' daily life.

4. Discuss the expansion of Muslim rule through military conquests and treaties, emphasizing the cultural blending within Muslim civilization and the spread and acceptance of Islam and the Arabic language.

5. Describe the growth of cities and the establishment of trade routes among Asia, Africa, and Europe, the products and inventions that traveled along these routes (e.g., spices, textiles, paper, steel, new crops), and the role of merchants in Arab society.

6. Understand the intellectual exchanges among Muslim scholars of Eurasia and Africa and the contributions Muslim scholars made to later civilizations in the areas of science, geography, mathematics, philosophy, medicine, art, and literature.

7.3 Students analyze the geographic, political, economic, religious, and social structures of the civilizations of China in the Middle Ages.

1. Describe the reunification of China under the Tang Dynasty and reasons for the spread of Buddhism in Tang China, Korea, and Japan.

2. Describe agricultural, technological, and commercial developments during the Tang and Sung periods.

3. Analyze the influences of Confucianism and changes in Confucian thought during the Sung and Mongol periods.

4. Understand the importance of both overland trade and maritime expeditions between China and other civilizations in the Mongol Ascendancy and Ming Dynasty.

5. Trace the historic influence of such discoveries as tea, the manufacture of paper, wood-block printing, the compass, and gunpowder.

6. Describe the development of the imperial state and the scholar-official class.

7.4 Students analyze the geographic, political, economic, religious, and social structures of the sub-Saharan civilizations of Ghana and Mali in Medieval Africa.

1. Study the Niger River and the relationship of vegetation zones of forest, savannah, and desert to trade in gold, salt, food, and slaves; and the growth of the Ghana and Mali empires.

2. Analyze the importance of family, labor specialization, and regional commerce in the development of states and cities in West Africa.

California History–Social Science Content Standards and Analysis Skills ix

3. Describe the role of the trans-Saharan caravan trade in the changing religious and cultural characteristics of West Africa and the influence of Islamic beliefs, ethics, and law.

4. Trace the growth of the Arabic language in government, trade, and Islamic scholarship in West Africa.

5. Describe the importance of written and oral traditions in the transmission of African history and culture.

7.5 Students analyze the geographic, political, economic, religious, and social structures of the civilizations of Medieval Japan.

1. Describe the significance of Japan's proximity to China and Korea and the intellectual, linguistic, religious, and philosophical influence of those countries on Japan.

2. Discuss the reign of Prince Shotoku of Japan and the characteristics of Japanese society and family life during his reign.

3. Describe the values, social customs, and traditions prescribed by the lord-vassal system consisting of *shogun, daimyo,* and *samurai* and the lasting influence of the warrior code in the twentieth century.

4. Trace the development of distinctive forms of Japanese Buddhism.

5. Study the ninth and tenth centuries' golden age of literature, art, and drama and its lasting effects on culture today, including Murasaki Shikibu's *Tale of Genji*.

6. Analyze the rise of a military society in the late twelfth century and the role of the samurai in that society.

7.6 Students analyze the geographic, political, economic, religious, and social structures of the civilizations of Medieval Europe.

1. Study the geography of the Europe and the Eurasian land mass, including its location, topography, waterways, vegetation, and climate and their relationship to ways of life in Medieval Europe.

2. Describe the spread of Christianity north of the Alps and the roles played by the early church and by monasteries in its diffusion after the fall of the western half of the Roman Empire.

3. Understand the development of feudalism, its role in the medieval European economy, the way in which it was influenced by physical geography (the role of the manor and the growth of towns), and how feudal relationships provided the foundation of political order.

4. Demonstrate an understanding of the conflict and cooperation between the Papacy and European monarchs (e.g., Charlemagne, Gregory VII, Emperor Henry IV).

5. Know the significance of developments in medieval English legal and constitutional practices and their importance in the rise of modern democratic thought and representative institutions (e.g., Magna Carta, parliament, development of habeas corpus, and independent judiciary in England).

6. Discuss the causes and course of the religious Crusades and their effects on the Christian, Muslim, and Jewish populations in Europe, with emphasis on the increasing contact by Europeans with cultures of the Eastern Mediterranean world.

7. Map the spread of the bubonic plague from Central Asia to China, the Middle East, and Europe and describe its impact on global population.

8. Understand the importance of the Catholic church as a political, intellectual, and aesthetic institution (e.g., founding of universities, political and spiritual roles of the clergy, creation of monastic and mendicant religious orders, preservation of the Latin language and religious texts, St. Thomas Aquinas's synthesis of classical philosophy with Christian theology, and the concept of "natural law").

9. Know the history of the decline of Muslim rule in the Iberian Peninsula that culminated in the Reconquista and the rise of Spanish and Portuguese kingdoms.

7.7 Students compare and contrast the geographic, political, economic, religious, and social structures of the Meso-American and Andean civilizations.

1. Study the locations, landforms, and climates of Mexico, Central America, and South America and their effects on Mayan, Aztec, and Incan economies, trade, and development of urban societies.

2. Study the roles of people in each society, including class structures, family life, warfare, religious beliefs and practices, and slavery.

3. Explain how and where each empire arose and how the Aztec and Incan empires were defeated by the Spanish.

4. Describe the artistic and oral traditions and architecture in the three civilizations.

5. Describe the Meso-American achievements in astronomy and mathematics, including the development of the calendar and the Meso-American knowledge of seasonal changes to the civilizations' agricultural systems.

GRADE 7 History-Social Science Content Standards
Reporting Cluster 3: Renaissance/Reformation

7.8   Students analyze the origins, accomplishments, and geographic diffusion of the Renaissance.

1. Describe the way in which the revival of classical learning and the arts fostered a new interest in humanism (i.e., a balance between intellect and religious faith).

2. Explain the importance of Florence in the early stages of the Renaissance and the growth of independent trading cities (e.g., Venice), with emphasis on the cities' importance in the spread of Renaissance ideas.

3. Understand the effects of the reopening of the ancient "Silk Road" between Europe and China, including Marco Polo's travels and the location of his routes.

4. Describe the growth and effect of new ways of disseminating information (e.g., the ability to manufacture paper, translation of the Bible into the vernacular, printing).

5. Detail advances made in literature, the arts, science, mathematics, cartography, engineering, and the understanding of human anatomy and astronomy (e.g., by Dante Alighieri, Leonardo da Vinci, Michelangelo de Buonarroti Simoni, Johann Gutenberg, William Shakespeare).

7.9   Students analyze the historical developments of the Reformation.

1. List the causes for the internal turmoil in and weakening of the Catholic church (e.g., tax policies, selling of indulgences).

2. Describe the theological, political, and economic ideas of the major figures during the Reformation (e.g., Desiderius Erasmus, Martin Luther, John Calvin, William Tyndale).

3. Explain Protestants' new practices of church self-government and the influence of those practices on the development of democratic practices and ideas of federalism.

4. Identify and locate the European regions that remained Catholic and those became Protestant and explain how the division affected the distribution of religions in the New World.

5. Analyze how the Counter-Reformation revitalized the Catholic church and the forces that fostered the movement (e.g., St. Ignatius of Loyola and the Jesuits, the Council of Trent).

6. Understand the institution and impact of missionaries on Christianity and the diffusion of Christianity from Europe to other parts of the word in the medieval and early modern periods; locate missions on a world map.

7. Describe the Golden Age of cooperation between Jews and Muslims in medieval Spain that promoted creativity in art, literature, and science, including how that cooperation was terminated by the religious persecution of individuals and groups (e.g., the Spanish Inquisition and the expulsion of Jews and Muslims from Spain in 1492).

7.10   Students analyze the historical developments of the Scientific Revolution and its lasting effect on religious, political, and cultural institutions.

1. Discuss the roots of the Scientific Revolution (e.g., Greek rationalism; Jewish, Christian, and Muslim science; Renaissance humanism; new knowledge from global exploration).

2. Understand the significance of the new scientific theories (e.g., those of Copernicus, Galileo, Kepler, Newton) and the significance of new inventions (e.g., the telescope, microscope, thermometer, barometer).

3. Understand the scientific method advanced by Bacon and Descartes, the influence of new scientific rationalism on the growth of democratic ideas, and the coexistence of science with traditional religious beliefs.

7.11   Students analyze political and economic change in the sixteenth, seventeenth, and eighteenth centuries (the Age of Exploration, the Enlightenment, and the Age of Reason).

1. Know the great voyages of discovery, the locations of the routes, and the influence of cartography in the development of a new European worldview.

2. Discuss the exchanges of plants, animals, technology, culture, and ideas among Europe, Africa, Asia, and the Americas in the fifteenth and sixteenth centuries and the major economic and social effects on each continent.

3. Examine the origins of modern capitalism; the influence of mercantilism and cottage industry; the elements and importance of a market economy in seventeenth-century Europe; the changing international trading and marketing patterns, including their locations on a world map; and the influence of explorers and map makers.

4. Explain how the main ideas of the Enlightenment can be traced back to such movements as the Renaissance, the Reformation, and the Scientific Revolution and to the Greeks, Romans, and Christianity.

5. Describe how democratic thought and institutions were influenced by Enlightenment thinkers (e.g., John Locke, Charles-Louis Montesquieu, American founders).

6. Discuss how the principles in the Magna Carta were embodied in such documents as the English Bill of Rights and the American Declaration of Independence.

California History and Social Science Analysis Skills (Grades 6–8)

Chronological and Spatial Thinking

CST 1 Students explain how major events are related to one another in time.

CST 2 Students construct various time lines of key events, people, and periods of the historical era they are studying.

CST 3 Students use a variety of maps and documents to identify physical and cultural features of neighborhoods, cities, states, and countries and to explain the historical migration of people, expansion and disintegration of empires, and the growth of economic systems.

Research, Evidence, and Point of View

REP 1 Students frame questions that can be answered by historical study and research.

REP 2 Students distinguish fact from opinion in historical narratives and stories.

REP 3 Students distinguish relevant from irrelevant information, essential from incidental information, and verifiable from unverifiable information in historical narratives and stories.

REP 4 Students assess the credibility of primary and secondary sources and draw sound conclusions about them.

REP 5 Students detect the different historical points of view on historical events and determine the context in which the historical statements were made (the question asked, sources used, author's perspectives).

Historical Interpretation

HI 1 Students explain the central issues and problems from the past, placing people and events in a matrix of time and place.

HI 2 Students understand and distinguish cause, effect, sequence, and correlation in historical events, including the long-and short-term causal relations.

HI 3 Students explain the sources of historical continuity and how the combination of ideas and events explains the emergence of new patterns.

HI 4 Students recognize the role of chance, oversight, and error in history.

HI 5 Students recognize that interpretations of history are subject to change as new information is uncovered.

HI 6 Students interpret basic indicators or economic performance and conduct cost-benefit analyses of economic and political issues.

Quick Prep

This Quick Prep section provides a handy reference to key facts on a variety of topics in world history.

Major Eras in World History

The term era, or age, refers to a broad period of time characterized by a shared pattern of life. Eras and ages typically do not have exact starting and ending points. Because the historical development of different regions of the world is varied, no single listing of eras applies to all of world history. This chart applies primarily to Western civilization.

Era and Dates	Description
Stone Age (2.5 million–3000 B.C.)	This long prehistoric period is often divided into two parts: the Old Stone Age, or Paleolithic Age, and the New Stone Age, or Neolithic Age. The Paleolithic Age lasted from about 2.5 million to 8000 B.C. During this time, hominids made and used stone tools and learned to control fire. The Neolithic Age began about 8000 B.C., and ended about 3000 B.C., in some areas. In this period, people learned to polish stone tools, make pottery, grow crops, and raise animals. The introduction of agriculture, a major turning point in human history, is called the Neolithic Revolution.
Bronze Age (3000–1200 B.C.)	People began using bronze, rather than stone and copper, to make tools and weapons. The Bronze Age began in Sumer about 3000 B.C., when Sumerian metalworkers found that they could melt together certain amounts of copper and tin to make bronze. The first civilizations emerged during the Bronze Age.
Iron Age (1500–1000 B.C. to the present day)	The use of iron to make tools and weapons became widespread. The Iron Age is the last technological stage in the Stone-Bronze-Iron ages sequence.
Classical Greece (2000–300 B.C.)	Greek culture developed, rose to new heights, and spread to other lands. The Greek city-states established the first democratic governments. Greek scientists made advances in mathematics, medicine, and other fields. The Greeks produced great works of drama, poetry, sculpture, architecture, and philosophy that still influence people today.
Roman Empire (500 B.C.–A.D. 500)	At its height, the Roman Empire united much of Europe, the north coast of Africa, and a large part of the Middle East. The Romans admired Greek art, literature, architecture, and science, and so they adopted and preserved much of Greek culture. The Romans also created their own legacy with outstanding achievements in engineering, architecture, the arts, and law. The Romans spread Christianity throughout Europe, and their official language—Latin—gave rise to French, Italian, Spanish, and other Romance languages. Western civilization has its roots in Greco-Roman culture.
Middle Ages (500–1200)	The West Roman Empire fell to Germanic conquerors who formed kingdoms out of former Roman provinces. A new political and military system called feudalism became established. Nobles were granted the use of lands that belonged to their king in exchange for their loyalty, military service, and protection of the peasants who worked the land. Western Europe became divided into feudal states. The Middle Ages was the time of castles and knights.
Renaissance and Reformation (1300–1600)	The Renaissance was a period of rebirth of learning and the arts based on a revival of classical study. The study of Greek classics gave rise to an intellectual movement called humanism, which emphasized human potential and achievements rather than religious concerns. The works of the Italian artists Leonardo da Vinci and Michelangelo and the English dramatist William Shakespeare represent the cultural height of the Renaissance. The Reformation was a movement for religious reform that led to the founding of Protestant churches. These churches rejected the authority of the pope. The power of the Roman Catholic Church declined.
Exploration and Colonization (1400–1800)	The monarchs of Europe financed voyages around the world, motivated by the desire for riches and the hope of spreading Christianity. Seeking spices and converts, European explorers made long sea journeys to the East. Searching for a shorter sea route to Asia, Christopher Columbus landed in the Caribbean islands and opened up the New World to European colonization. The establishment of colonies and trading networks led to worldwide cultural exchange, but also to the devastation of Native American cultures in the New World, and the enslavement of millions of Africans.
Revolution and Independence (1700–1900)	Movements toward democracy and nationalism affected most countries in the Western world. These movements sparked the Revolutionary War in America, which resulted in the independence of the British colonies and the birth of the United States. They also sparked the ten-year French Revolution. Many Latin American nations fought colonial rule and gained their independence. In Europe, great empires fell and a system of nation-states became established.

Major Empires

Name and Dates	Location	Achievements
Akkadian (c. 2350–2150 B.C.)	Mesopotamia	Became the world's first empire
Alexandrian (336–322 B.C.)	Greece, Persia, Egypt, northwest India	Spread Greek culture
Assyrian (c. 850–612 B.C.)	Southwest Asia, Egypt	Built one of the ancient world's largest libraries at Nineveh, the largest city of its day
Athenian	Greece	Developed democratic principles and classical culture
Austro-Hungarian (late 1600s–1918)	Central Europe	Became known for its cultural life, especially its great composers
Aztec (1325–1521)	Mesoamerica	Built pyramids and developed a pictorial written language
British (1600s–1980s)	United Kingdom, Americas, Africa, Asia	Held one-fourth of the world's land and spread British culture to one-fourth of the world's people
Byzantine (395–1453)	Parts of southern and eastern Europe, northern Africa, and the Middle East	Preserved Greek culture, Roman customs, and Christianity and built the Hagia Sophia
Egyptian (2780–1075 B.C.)	Egypt, Nubia, parts of Syria and Palestine	Built magnificent palaces, temples, and pyramids
Ghana (800–1076)	West Africa	Became a center of the gold-salt trade
Han (201 B.C.–A.D. 220)	China	Established a centralized, bureaucratic government and unified Chinese culture
Holy Roman (962–1806)	Western and central Europe	Was the strongest state in Europe until about 1100
Inca (1400–1532)	South America	Built a vast empire linked by an extensive road system
Mali (1200–1400)	West Africa	Became wealthy on the gold-salt trade and created an efficient government
Maya (250–900)	Mesoamerica	Built pyramids and developed the most advanced writing system in the ancient Americas
Mongol (about 1200–1294)	Europe, Asia	Created the largest unified land empire in history
Mughal (1526–1700s)	India	Built unique architecture, including the Taj Mahal
Muslim (661–1258)	Southwest Asia, North Africa	Spread scholarship and written culture
Old Babylonian (about 2000–1550 B.C.)	Mesopotamia	Compiled the Code of Hammurabi
Ottoman (about 1300–1922)	Turkey, North Africa, Southwest Asia, Southeast Europe	Became the world's most powerful empire in the 1500s and 1600s and built architectural masterpieces
Persian (about 550–330 B.C.)	Fertile Crescent, Anatolia, Egypt, India	Established a judicious, thoughtful, and tolerant government
Roman (27 B.C.–A.D. 476)	Europe, Mesopotamia, North Africa	Spread Greek and Roman culture, which became the basis of Western civilization
Songhai (1460s–1591)	West Africa	Gained control of trans-Saharan trade routes and built a thriving empire

Major Geographic Features

United States and Canada

Climate		Vegetation		Land Forms and Bodies of Water	
Arctic	Semi-arid	Tundra	Mediterranean	Great Lakes	Rocky Mountains
Sub-arctic	Sub-tropical	Coniferous forest	scrub	Gulf of Mexico	Mississippi River
Temperate	Tropical	Broadleaf forest	Semi-desert	Appalachian	
Arid		Grassland	Desert	Mountains	

Latin America

Climate		Vegetation		Land Forms and Bodies of Water	
Tropical	Temperate	Savannah	Tropical rainforest	Orinoco River	Sierra Madre
Sub-tropical	Arid	Semi-desert	Monsoon forest	Andes Mountains	Amazon River
Desert	Semi-arid	Desert	Broadleaf forest		
		Dry tropical scrub			

Europe, Russia, and the Independent Republics

Climate		Vegetation		Land Forms and Bodies of Water	
Sub-arctic	Temperate	Tundra	Grassland	Baltic Sea	Volga River
Steppe	Mediterranean	Coniferous forest	Mediterranean	Mediterranean Sea	Alps Mountains
Tundra	Alpine	Broadleaf forest	scrub	North Sea	Pyrenees
Humid continental				Lake Baikal	Mountains
				Danube River	Ural Mountains
				Rhine River	

North Africa and Southwest Asia

Climate		Vegetation		Land Forms and Bodies of Water	
Desert	Temperate	Semi-desert	Monsoon forest	Red Sea	Sahara Desert
Sub-tropical	Arid	Desert	Dry tropical scrub	Persian Gulf	Nile River
Tropical	Semi-arid			Black Sea	Tigris River
Tropical monsoon				Dead Sea	Euphrates River

Africa South of the Sahara

Climate		Vegetation		Land Forms and Bodies of Water	
Tropical	Semi-arid	Savannah	Dry tropical scrub	Mount Kilimanjaro	Congo River
Sub-tropical	Desert	Semi-desert	Tropical rainforest	Kalahari Desert	Niger River
Arid		Desert	Monsoon forest	Victoria Falls	Zambezi River
				Nile River	

Southern Asia

Climate		Vegetation		Land Forms and Bodies of Water	
Tropical	Sub-tropical	Monsoon forest	Sub-tropical forest	Himalayan	Mekong River
Monsoon	Moderate	Tropical rainforest		Mountains	Arabian Sea
				Mount Everest	South China Sea
				Indus River	Bay of Bengal
				Ganges River	Malay Archipelago

East Asia, Australia, and the Pacific Islands

Climate		Vegetation		Land Forms and Bodies of Water	
Temperate	Sub-tropical	Savannah	Dry tropical scrub	Mount Fuji	Huang He
Arid	Tropical	Semi-desert	Tropical rainforest	Southern Alps	(Yellow River)
Semi-arid		Desert	Monsoon forest	Gobi Desert	Chang Jiang
				Great Barrier Reef	(Yangtze River)

Major Figures in World History

Name and Dates	Location	Achievements
Abraham (2000 B.C.?)	Hebrew leader	Founded Judaism
Alexander the Great (356–323 B.C.)	Macedonian king	Built an empire that included Greece, Persia, Egypt, and part of Central Asia
Aristotle (384–322 B.C.)	Greek philosopher	Summarized most knowledge up to his time and invented rules of logic that contributed to the modern scientific method
Augustus (63 B.C.–A.D. 14)	Roman emperor	Ruled the Roman Empire at its peak
Caesar, Julius (100–44 B.C.)	Roman general and dictator	Expanded the Roman Empire
Catherine the Great (1729–1796)	Russian empress	Expanded the Russian Empire
Charlemagne (742–814)	Frankish emperor	United much of Western Europe in the Carolingian Empire
Columbus, Christopher (1451–1506)	Genoese navigator	Led sea voyages that opened the New World to European colonization
Confucius (551–479 B.C.)	Chinese scholar	Founded Confucianism
Constantine the Great (A.D. 285?–337)	Roman emperor	Ended the persecution of Christians and moved the capital of the Roman Empire to Byzantium, which was renamed Constantinople
Cortés, Hernando (1485–1547)	Spanish conqueror	Conquered the Aztec empire of Mexico
Elizabeth I (1533–1603)	English queen	Reigned over the English Renaissance, also called the Elizabethan Age after her
Euclid (330?–270? B.C.)	Hellenistic mathematician	Called the father of geometry for compiling the mathematics textbook *The Elements*
Gutenberg, Johannes (1400?–1468?)	German printer	Invented movable metal type
Hammurabi (?–1750 B.C.)	Babylonian king	Built the first great Babylonian Empire and compiled one of the first written collections of laws, the Code of Hammurabi
Hannibal (247–183 B.C.)	Carthaginian general	Led troops and elephants across the Alps to fight Rome in the Second Punic War
Henry VIII (1491–1547)	English king	Separated the Church of England from the Roman Catholic Church
Jefferson, Thomas (1743–1826)	American president, architect, and inventor	Wrote the Declaration of Independence
Jesus (4 B.C.?–A.D. 28?)	Jewish religious leader	Founded Christianity
Khan, Genghis (1162?–1227)	Mongol ruler	Started the Mongol Empire
Khan, Kublai (1215–1294)	Mongol ruler	Conquered China and made it part of the Mongol Empire
Locke, John (1632–1704)	English philosopher	Was a leader of the Enlightenment and promoted democratic thinking

Name and Dates	Location	Achievements
Luther, Martin (1483–1546)	German theologian	Started the Reformation
Michelangelo (1475–1564)	Italian artist	Was a leader in the Italian Renaissance and is considered one of the greatest artists of all time
Moses (1300s B.C.?)	Israelite leader	Led the Jews out of Egypt and received the Ten Commandments
Muhammad (A.D. 570?–632)	Muslim prophet	Founded Islam
Pericles (494?–429 B.C.)	Greek statesman	Led Athens during its golden age, often called the Age of Pericles
Plato (427–347 B.C.)	Greek philosopher	Wrote *The Republic,* in which he described his ideal society
Siddhartha Gautama (563?–483 B.C.)	Buddhist monk	Founded Buddhism
Socrates (469–399 B.C.)	Greek philosopher	Taught students to examine their beliefs and developed a question-and-answer method of teaching called the Socratic method
Voltaire (1694–1778)	French writer and philosopher	Was a leading writer of the Enlightenment
Washington, George (1732–1799)	American general and president	Commanded the Continental Army during the Revolutionary War and served as the first president of the United States

Major Events in World History

Time and Place	Event	Significance
40,000 B.C. Europe	Cro-Magnons appear.	Ancestors of modern humans
8000 B.C. Africa, Asia	Agriculture begins.	One of the great breakthroughs in human history, setting the stage for the development of civilizations
3100 B.C. Egypt	Upper and Lower Egypt unite.	The Kingdom of Egypt, ruled by pharaohs, began a 3,000-year period of unity and cultural continuity.
3000 B.C. Mesopotamia	Civilization emerges in Sumer.	One of the world's first civilizations
2500 B.C. Indus Valley	Planned cities arise.	Beginning of the Indus Valley civilization; many features of modern Indian culture can be traced to this early civilization.
2350 B.C. Mesopotamia	Sargon of Akkad builds an empire.	World's first empire, which extended from the Mediterranean coast in the west to present-day Iran in the east
1700 B.C. Asian steppes	Indo-Europeans begin migrations.	The Indo-Europeans moved into Europe, the Middle East, and India, spreading their languages and changing cultures.
1532 B.C. China	Shang Dynasty begins.	The first Chinese civilization, which arose along the Huang He river
1200 B.C. Mexico	Olmec culture arises.	Oldest known civilization in the Americas
1000 B.C. Africa	Bantu migrations begin.	Bantu speakers spread their language and culture throughout southern Africa.
850 B.C. Assyria	Assyria builds an empire.	Using military force to conquer and rule, the Assyrians established an empire that included most of the old centers of power in Southwest Asia and Egypt.
800 B.C. Greece	Greek city-states arise.	Led to the development of several political systems, including democracy
550 B.C. Persia	Cyrus builds the Persian Empire.	Characterized by tolerance and wise government
500 B.C. Rome	Romans establish a republic.	Source of some of the most fundamental values and institutions of Western civilization
461 B.C. Greece	Age of Pericles begins.	Democratic principles and classical Greek culture flourished, leaving a legacy that endures to the present day.
334 B.C. Greece	Alexander begins to build an empire.	Conquered Persia and Egypt; extended his empire to the Indus River in India; resulted in a blending of Greek, Egyptian, and Eastern customs
321 B.C. India	Mauryan Empire is established.	United north India politically for the first time
202 B.C. China	Han Dynasty replaces Qin dynasty.	Expanded China's borders; developed a system of government that lasted for centuries
27 B.C. Rome	Octavian rules Roman Empire.	Took the title of Augustus and ruled the mightiest empire of the ancient world; began the Pax Romana, a 200-year period of peace and prosperity; Roman way of life spread throughout the empire.
A.D. 29 Jerusalem	Jesus is crucified.	Christianity spread throughout the Roman Empire.
A.D. 100 South America	Moche civilization emerges.	Built an advanced society in Peru
A.D. 320 India	Gupta Empire begins.	A great flowering of Indian civilization, especially Hindu culture
A.D. 527 Constantinople	Justinian I becomes Byzantine emperor.	Recovered and ruled almost all the former territory of the Roman Empire; created a body of civil laws called Justinian's Code; built beautiful churches

Copyright © McDougal Littell/Houghton Mifflin Company

Time and Place	Event	Significance
618 China	Tang dynasty begins.	Created a powerful empire, improved trade and agriculture, and restored the civil service bureaucracy
600 Central America	Maya civilization thrives.	Built spectacular cities and developed the most advanced writing system in the ancient Americas
800 North America	Anasazi civilization develops.	Ancestors of the Pueblo peoples
800s–900s West Africa	Empire of Ghana thrives.	Built its wealth on the trans-Saharan gold-salt trade
814 Western Europe	Charlemagne unites much of Europe.	Established the Carolingian Empire
960 China	Sung Dynasty begins.	China became the most populous and advanced country in the world.
1095 France	Pope Urban II issues call for First Crusade.	Stimulated trade, weakened the power of the pope and feudal nobles, and left a legacy of distrust between Christians and Muslims
1192 Japan	Kamakura Shogunate begins.	First shogunate, which set the pattern for military dictators, called shoguns, to rule Japan until 1868
1200s Mexico	Aztec civilization begins.	Built the greatest empire in Mesoamerica
1200s Peru	Inca Empire begins.	The largest empire in the Americas
1209 Mongolia	Genghis Khan begins Mongol conquests.	Built the largest unified land empire in world history
1215 England	King John agrees to Magna Carta.	The Magna Carta contributed to modern concepts of jury trials and legal rights.
1235 Africa	Sundiata founds Mali Empire.	Became a powerful center of commerce and trade in West Africa
1279 China	Kublai Khan conquers Sung Dynasty.	Completed the conquest of China and encouraged trade; Chinese ideas then began to influence Western civilization.
1300 Italy	Renaissance begins.	Revival of classical studies revolutionized art, literature, and society
1337 France	Hundred Years' War begins.	Ended the Middle Ages
1347 Italy	Bubonic plague spreads to Europe.	Killed nearly one-third of Europe's population and disrupted medieval society
1368 China	Ming Dynasty begins.	Ended Mongol rule of China and made China the dominant power in the region
1453 Turkey	Constantinople falls to Turks.	One of the most influential cities of the 15th century, Constantinople became part of the Ottoman Empire, and its name was changed to Istanbul.
1492 Americas	Columbus sails to Hispaniola.	Opened the way for European settlement of the Americas
1517 Germany	Martin Luther begins Reformation.	Led to the founding of Protestant churches
1526 India	Babur founds Mughal Empire.	Brought Turks, Persians, and Indians together in a vast empire
1529 Anatolia	Suleiman the Magnificent rules Ottoman Empire.	The Ottoman Empire reached its greatest size and grandeur.
1603 Japan	Tokugawa Shogunate begins.	Unified Japan and began a 200-year period of isolation and prosperity
1607 North America	English settle at Jamestown.	England's first permanent settlement in North America

Major Religions

	Buddhism	Christianity	Hinduism	Islam	Judaism	Confucianism
Followers worldwide (estimated 2003 figures)	364 million	2 billion	828 million	1.2 billion	14.5 million	6.3 million
Name of god	no god	God	Brahman	Allah	God	no god
Founder	the Buddha	Jesus	no founder	no founder but spread by Muhammad	Abraham	Confucius
Holy book	many sacred books, including the Dhammapada	Bible, including Old Testament and New Testament	many sacred texts, including the Upanishads	Qur'an	Hebrew Bible, including the Torah	*Analects*
Clergy	Buddhist monks	priests, ministers, monks, and nuns	Brahmin priests, monks, and gurus	no clergy but a scholar class, called the ulama, and imams, who may lead prayers	rabbis	no clergy
Basic beliefs	• Followers can achieve enlightenment by understanding The Four Noble Truths and by following The Noble Eightfold Path of right opinions, right desires, right speech, right action, right job, right effort, right concentration, and right meditation.	• There is only one God, who watches over and cares for his people. • Jesus is the Son of God. He died to save humanity. His death and resurrection made eternal life possible for others.	• The soul never dies but is continually reborn until it becomes divinely enlightened. • Persons achieve happiness and divine enlightenment after they free themselves from their earthly desires. • Freedom from earthly desires comes from many lifetimes of worship, knowledge, and virtuous acts.	• Persons achieve salvation by following the Five Pillars of Islam and living a just life. The pillars are faith, prayer, charity, fasting, and pilgrimage to Mecca.	• There is only one God, who watches over and cares for his people. • God loves and protects his people but also holds people accountable for their sins and shortcomings. • Persons serve God by studying the Torah and living by its teachings.	• Social order, harmony, and good government should be based on strong family relationships. • Respect for parents and elders is important to a well-ordered society. • Education is important for the welfare of both the individual and society.

° estimated 2002 figures

Major Inventions Through 1750

Some dates are approximate, some are historically debated.

Invention	Date	Significance
Irrigation	5000 B.C.	Brought water to crops; led to settled living and rise of early civilizations
Copper Working	5000 B.C.	First evidence of metal work, led to bronze work and later, iron work
Loom	4400 B.C.	Enabled people to weave cloth
Wheel	3800 B.C.	Easier and further transport of loads; became a part of vehicles and machines
Writing	3500 B.C.	Enabled record keeping, communication, shared history and scholarship
Plow	3000 B.C.	Made farming more productive
Glass Working	2500 B.C.	Primarily decorative; later used in containers, windows, and lenses
Musical Notation	1300 B.C.	Enabled shared musical culture
Aqueduct	700 B.C.	Brought water to cities, led to larger better-planned cities
Catapult	400 B.C.	Used for defense and war; allowed larger and further launch of weapons
Magnetic Compass	300s B.C.	Used for navigation; helped make longer sea voyages possible
Papermaking	100 B.C.	Spread written information and scholarship
Abacus	A.D. 190	Allowed quick accurate calculation including square and cube roots
Algebra; Zero; Decimal Place	500	Enabled abstract clacluations and better recordkeeping
Windmill	600	Power for grinding grain, pumping water; later used to generate electric power
Gunpowder	800s	Used in fireworks, bombs; influenced weapons development; later used in guns
Magnifying Glass	1250	Used for study of small matter and used in crafts
Gun / Cannon	1260	Enabled weapons to be used at long range for better defense
Mechanical Clock	1360	Allowed better planning, especially in cities and in traveling
Printing Press	1454	Spread written information, scholarship, and new ideas, especially in religion
Cast Iron Pipe	1455	A conduit for water and sewage; improved sanitation
Graphite Pencil	1560	Helped in art, science, mathematics and education for drafting ideas
Microscope	1590	Allowed study of cells and microorganisms; new knowledge of life processes
Telescope	1608	Study of the stars, planets, objects, and motion in space; better navigation
Submarine	1620	Used for ocean exploration and later for warfare
Analytic Geometry	1637	System for describing points, planes, and curves in abstract space
Steam Engine	1639	Helped start and power the industrial revloution
Barometer	1643	Measured atmospheric pressure; allowed more accurate weather prediction
Tourniquet	1674	Used in medicine to apply pressure and stop blood flow to a part of the body
Piano	1709	Produced a greater range of sounds than previous musical instruments
Mercury Thermometer	1714	Measured heat by degrees; improved chemistry, meteorology, and medicine
Ship Chronometer	1728	Allowed timekeeping at sea; led to longitude measurements; improved mapping
Threshing Machine	1732	Sped up crop production; improved farming
Classification of Species	1735	Allowed shared data about global discoveries within a scientific naming system
Wool Carding Machine	1743	Sped production of fibers for wool cloth
Leyden Jar	1746	First electrical condensor, led to understanding of current and circuits
Dynamometer	1750	Measured mechanical forces, used in developing new machines

Major Explorations

Area Explored	Dates	Explorer(s)	Nationality
Newfoundland	about 1000	Leif Ericson	Norse
China, Southeast Asia, India	1270s–1290s	Marco Polo	Venetian
West Indies, South and Central America	1492–1502	Christopher Columbus	Italian
Newfoundland	1497	John and Sebastian Cabot	Italian
Cape of Good Hope, Africa; India	1497–1498	Vasco da Gama	Portuguese
East and north coast of South America	1497–1499	Vespucci	Italian
Brazil	1500	Pedro Alvarez Cabral	Portuguese
Panama, Pacific Ocean	1513	Vasco Nunez de Balboa	Spanish
Florida, Yucatán Peninsula	1513	Juan Ponce de Leon	Spanish
Mexico	1519	Hernando Cortés	Spanish
Straits of Magellan, Tierra del Fuego	1519–1520	Ferdinand Magellan	Portuguese
New York harbor	1524	Giovanni da Verrazano	Italian
Texas	1528	Cabeza de Vaca	Spanish
Peru	1532	Francisco Pizarro	Spanish
Canada, Gulf of St. Lawrence	1534	Jacques Cartier	French
Buenos Aires	1536	Pedro de Mendoza	Spanish
Mississippi River, near Memphis	1539–1541	Hernando de Soto	Spanish
Southwestern United States	1540	Francisco de Coronado	Spanish
Colorado River	1540	Hernando Alarcon	Spanish
Colorado, Grand Canyon	1540	Garcia de Lopez Cardenas	Spanish
Amazon River	1541	Francisco de Orellana	Spanish
Western Mexico, San Diego harbor	1542	Juan Rodriguez Cabrillo	Portuguese
California coast	1577–1580	Sir Francis Drake	English
Orinoco river	1595	Sir Walter Raleigh	English
Canadian interior, Lake Champlain	1603–1609	Samuel de Champlain	French
Hudson River, Hudson Bay	1609–1610	Henry Hudson	English
Tasmania	1642	Abel Janszoon	Dutch
Mississippi River, south to Arkansas	1673	Jacques Marquette, Louis Joliet	French
Mississippi River, south to Gulf of Mexico	1682	Robert Cavelier, sieur de La Salle	French
Bering Strait and Alaska	1727–1729	Vitus Bering	Danish
South Pacific	1768–1775	James Cook	English
Northwestern Canada	1789	Sir Alexander Mackenzie	Canadian
Missouri River, Rocky Mountains, Columbia River	1804–1805	Meriwether Lewis, William Clark	American
Arabia, East Africa, Lake Tanganyika	1853–1858	Sir Richard Burton	English
Upper course of Zambezi River, Victoria Falls, Lake Ngami	1849–1873	David Livingstone	Scottish
Congo River	1874–1889	Sir Henry Stanley	Welsh
North Pole	1909	Robert E. Peary, Matthew Henson	American
South Pole	1911	Roald Amundsen	Norwegian
Moon	1969	Neil Armstrong, Edwin Aldrin	American
Mars	1975	Space probes Viking 1 and 2	American

Major World Documents

Time and Place	Event	Significance
Analects (about 400 B.C.)	Followers of Confucius	Teachings of Confucius
Bill of Rights (adopted 1791)	Members of Congress	First 10 amendments to the U.S. Constitution, outlining the rights and liberties of American citizens
Code of Hammurabi (1700s B.C.)	Hammurabi	Collection of laws for Babylonian Empire
Dead Sea Scrolls (about 200 B.C.–A.D. 70)	Probably the Essenes, a Jewish sect	Ancient manuscripts from Palestine that include the oldest manuscript of the Hebrew Bible
Declaration of Independence (1776)	Thomas Jefferson	Statement of the American colonists' reasons for declaring independence from Great Britain
Declaration of the Rights of Man (1789)	French National Assembly	Statement of the rights of French men
English Bill of Rights (1689)	English Parliament	List of the rights of Englishmen
Hebrew Bible (after 1000 B.C.)	Unknown	Sacred book of Judaism
Justinian Code (A.D. 528–533)	Panel of legal experts appointed by Byzantine emperor Justinian	Collection of early Roman laws and legal opinions
Magna Carta (1215)	English nobles	Guaranteed rights of English nobles
Mayflower Compact (1620)	Pilgrim leaders	First written agreement for self-government in America
New Testament (after about A.D. 70)	Unknown	Sacred book of Christianity
Ninety-Five Theses (1517)	Martin Luther	Statements addressing problems within the Catholic Church
Popol Vuh (1500s)	Unknown	Creation story of the Maya
Qur'an (A.D. 610–632)	Considered to be revelations from the angel Gabriel to Muhammad	Sacred book of Muslims
The Republic (375 B.C.?)	Plato	Description of ideal state of society
Two Treatises of Government (1690)	John Locke	Ideas on government and natural rights
U.S. Constitution (adopted 1788)	Members of Constitutional Convention	Statement of the form of the United States government
Vedas (about 1400 B.C.)	Unknown	Sacred books of Hinduism

Government and Economic Systems

Government Systems		
System	**Definition**	**Example**
aristocracy	Power is in the hands of a hereditary ruling class or nobility.	Medieval Europe
autocracy	A single person rules with unlimited power. Autocracy is also called dictatorship and despotism.	Pharaohs of ancient Egypt
democracy	Citizens hold political power either directly or through representatives. In a direct democracy, citizens directly make political decisions. In a representative democracy, the citizens rule through elected representatives.	ancient Athens (direct democracy) United States since the 1700s (representative democracy)
federalism	Powers are divided among the federal, or national, government and a number of state governments.	United States since the 1700s
feudalism	A king allows nobles to use his land in exchange for their loyalty, military service, and protection of the people who live on the land.	Medieval Europe
military state	Military leaders rule, supported by the power of the armed forces.	Assyrian Empire
monarchy	A ruling family headed by a king or queen holds political power and may or may not share the power with citizen bodies. In an absolute monarchy, the ruling family has all the power. In a limited or constitutional monarchy, the ruler's power is limited by the constitution or laws of the nation.	reign of King Louis XIV of France (absolute monarchy) United Kingdom (constitutional monarchy)
oligarchy	A few persons or a small group rule.	most ancient Greek city-states
parliamentary	Legislative and executive functions are combined in a legislature called a parliament.	United Kingdom since the 1200s
presidential	The chief officer is a president who is elected independently of the legislature.	United States since the 1700s
republic	Citizens elect representatives to rule on their behalf.	Roman Republic
theocracy	Religious leaders control the government, relying on religious law and consultation with religious scholars. In early theocracies, the ruler was considered divine.	Aztec Empire
totalitarianism	The government controls every aspect of public and private life and all opposition is suppressed.	Soviet Union under Joseph Stalin

Economic Systems

System	Definition	Example
command	The production of goods and services is determined by a central government, which usually owns the means of production. Also called a planned economy.	former Soviet Union
communism	All means of production—land, mines, factories, railroads, and businesses—are owned by the people, private property does not exist, and all goods and services are shared equally.	former Soviet Union
free enterprise	Businesses are privately owned and operate competitively for profit, with minimal government interference. Also called capitalism.	United States
manorialism	A lord gives serfs land, shelter, and protection in exchange for work, and almost everything needed for daily life is produced on the manor, or lord's estate.	Medieval Europe
market	The production of goods and services is determined by the demand from consumers. Also called a demand economy.	United States
mixed	A combination of command and market economies is designed to provide goods and services so that all people will benefit.	present-day Israel
socialism	The means of production are owned by the public and operate for the welfare of all.	In many present-day countries, including Denmark and Sweden, the government owns some industries and operates them for the public good.
traditional	Goods and services are exchanged without the use of money; also called barter.	many ancient civilizations and tribal societies

Key Terms and Names

TERMS

Age of Reason a period beginning in the late 1600s and peaking in the 1700s in which reason was relied upon to produce truths about human nature.

Allah God in the Islamic religion.

astronomy the study of planets, stars, and other celestial bodies.

bubonic plague a disease that struck western Eurasia in the mid-1300s, in an outbreak known as the Black Death.

bureaucracy a system of departments and agencies that carry out the work of a government.

bushido the code of conduct of samurai warriors, which required that they be generous, brave, and loyal.

caliph a ruler of the Muslim community, viewed as a successor of Muhammad.

cartography the skills and methods used in the making of maps.

codex a book of the type used by early Meso-American civilizations to record important historical events.

Columbian Exchange the movement of plants, animals, and other living things between the eastern and western hemispheres after Columbus's voyage to the Americas in 1492.

cottage industry system of manufacturing in which families produced goods in their homes, which were then sold by merchants.

Council of Trent a group of high level Catholic Church officials who met from 1545 to 1563 to work on reforming the church.

Counter Reformation a 16th-century movement in which the Roman Catholic Church instituted new policies in response to the Protestant Reformation.

Crusades a series of military expeditions from Christian Europe to Palestine between the 11th and 13th centuries.

cultural diffusion the spread of ethnic ideas and customs to other areas of the world.

daimyo a Japanese lord with large landholdings and a private samurai army, who paid no taxes to the government.

Eastern Orthodox Church a branch of Christianity that developed in the Byzantine Empire and is not under the authority of the pope.

Enlightenment a philosophical movement in the 17th and 18th centuries in which philosophers used reason to understand truths about human nature.

federalism the sharing of power between an organization or government and its members.

golden age a period in which a society or culture is at its peak.

griot an official storyteller in an African civilization.

habeas corpus the right of people not to be imprisoned unlawfully.

Hindu-Arabic numerals the numerals used in the United States and western Europe, which originated in India.

humanism a movement in Renaissance Europe, celebrating human potential and achievement and stressing the study of subjects such as history, grammar, literature, and philosophy.

Iberian Peninsula the southwestern tip of Europe, where the modern nations of Spain and Portugal are located.

imperial state highly organized bureaucratic government in China developed during the Tang dynasty.

independent judiciary court system that operates without influence from other branches of the government.

indulgence the relaxation of earthly penalty for sin.

Inquisition a court established by the Roman Catholic Church to investigate people who may have strayed from the Roman Catholic faith and to strengthen the power of the Church.

Jesuit a member of the Society of Jesus, a religious order founded in the early 1530s by St. Ignatius of Loyola.

labor specialization the doing of specific types of work by trained or knowledgeable workers.

lord a powerful landholding noble.

manor the estate of a feudal noble, usually including a fortified building or castle.

mercantilism an economic policy based on the idea that a nation's power depends on its wealth.

Meso-America a region that includes the southern part of Mexico and much of Central America.

Ming Dynasty the dynasty that assumed control of China in 1368 and restored China's imperial state.

missionary a person who travels to a foreign country in order to do religious work.

monastery a place where members of a religious order practice a life of prayer and worship.

Mongol Ascendancy the period in which the Mongols controlled all of Central Asia, making overland trade and travel safe.

Muslim a person who follows the religion of Islam, accepting Allah as the only God.

natural law a rule of conduct inferred from nature that governs people's actions in addition to or in place of laws handed down by human authority.

natural rights the rights that all people are born with—such as the rights to life, liberty, and property according to the Enlightenment philosopher John Locke.

nomad a person who moves from place to place rather than settling permanently.

parliament a group of representatives with some powers of government.

philosophy an investigation of basic truths about the universe, based on logical reasoning.

Protestant a member of a Christian group that broke with the Roman Catholic Church during or after the 16th century.

rationalism the idea that people should use reason, or logical thought, to understand the world.

Reconquista the series of campaigns, ending in 1492, by which Christian armies drove Muslim rulers out of Spain.

Reformation a movement of opposition to the Roman Catholic Church, beginning in the 16th century.

Roman Catholic relating to the Christian church of the West that is under the authority of the pope.

samurai a trained warrior of the Japanese aristocracy.

savannah a flat grassland, with few trees, in a tropical region.

scholar-official an educated person with a government position.

scientific method an approach to scientific investigation that involves making careful observations, forming and testing a hypothesis, and drawing a conclusion that confirms or modifies the hypothesis.

Scientific Revolution a period, beginning in the 1500s, during which European scholars began to question classical scientific ideas and Christian beliefs.

shogun a Japanese military leader—one of a group that first came to power in 1192 and ruled on the emperor's behalf but usually in their own interests.

Silk Roads the ancient trade routes that connected Europe with China.

Sung Dynasty period in China from 960 to 1279 in which trade and agriculture flourished.

Sunnah Muhammad's words and deeds, which serve Muslims as a guide for proper living.

Tang Dynasty period in China from 618 to the 900s during which time the imperial state was developed and China's unity was strengthened.

trans-Saharan across the Sahara.

vassal in feudal society, a person who received land and protection from a lord in return for loyalty.

vegetation zone a region that, because of its soil and climate, has distinctive types of plants.

vernacular a person's native language.

wood-block printing a printing system developed by the ancient Chinese, in which wood blocks were carved with enough characters to print entire pages.

worldview understanding and belief about the universe held by a group of people.

Zen a Japanese form of Buddhism, focusing on self-discipline, simplicity, and meditation.

NAMES

Alighieri, Dante (1265–1321) Italian author of *The Divine Comedy,* who influenced other writers to use the vernacular.

Aquinas, Thomas (1224–1274) Italian scholar who made a synthesis of classical philosophy and Christian theology.

Bacon, Sir Francis (1561–1626) English philosopher whose emphasis on experimentation influenced the development of the scientific method.

Calvin, John (1509–1564) A leader of the Protestant Reformation who emphasized the doctrine of predestination.

Charlemagne (742–814) King of the Franks (from 768) who conquered much of Europe and spread Christianity in the conquered regions.

Constantine (285–337) Roman emperor from A.D. 306 to 337, who ended the persecution of Christians and moved the capital of the empire to Byzantium (later known as Constantinople).

Copernicus, Nicolaus (1473–1543) Polish astronomer who proposed the theory that the earth and other planets revolve around the sun.

Descartes, René (1596–1650) French philosopher whose emphasis on rationalism influenced the development of the scientific method.

Erasmus, Desiderius (1469–1536) Renaissance humanist who advocated reform within the Church.

Franklin, Benjamin (1706–1790) American inventor and statesman whose Enlightenment ideas contributed to the founding of the United States.

Galileo (1564–1642) Italian astronomer who first used a telescope to study the stars and who was persecuted for supporting Copernicus's theory that the sun was the center of the universe.

Gregory VII, Pope (1020–1085) Head of the Roman Catholic Church from 1073 to 1085, who struggled with Emperor Henry IV for power.

Gutenberg, Johannes (1400?–1468) German inventor of the printing press.

Henry IV, Emperor (1050–1106) 11th-century ruler of the Holy Roman Empire, who continually struggled for power with Pope Gregory VII.

Ignatius of Loyola (1491–1556) Spaniard who founded the religious order of Jesuits in the early 1530s.

John, King (1167–1216) King of England who signed the Magna Carta in 1215.

Kepler, Johannes (1571–1630) German astronomer and mathematician who described the elliptical orbits of the planets around the sun.

Leonardo da Vinci (1452–1519) Italian Renaissance painter who painted many masterpieces, such as the *Mona Lisa* and *The Last Supper*, and also excelled in scientific research.

Montesquieu, Charles-Louis (1689–1755) French noble and philosopher whose ideas about the separation of powers influenced the organization of the government of the United States.

Murasaki Shikibu, Lady (978–1014) Japanese writer whose work *The Tale of Genji* is considered one of the world's first novels.

Newton, Sir Isaac (1642–1727) English mathematician and scientist who formed the theory of universal gravitation.

Polo, Marco (1254–1324) Venetian trader who traveled the Silk Roads and arrived in China around 1275. He became an aide to Kublai Khan and later published a popular book about his adventures.

Shakespeare, William (1564–1616) Famous English writer of the Renaissance, best known for his plays *Romeo and Juliet* and *Hamlet*.

Shotoku, Prince (574–622) Regent who ruled Japan from 593 to 622 and brought elements of Chinese culture—in particular, the Buddhist religion—to the country.

Tyndale, William (1490–1536) English reformer who translated the New Testament into English.

Zheng He (1371–1435) Chinese admiral whose extensive voyages between 1405 and 1433 greatly expanded China's foreign trade and reputation.

REVIEW

**CALIFORNIA CONTENT
STANDARD 6.1**

Early Humankind

OVERALL OBJECTIVE: Describe what is known through archaeological studies of the early physical and cultural development of humankind from the Paleolithic era to the agricultural revolution.

Use the information and maps to answer questions on the next page.

2,000,000 B.C.

Hunter-Gatherers

- Relied on wild animals and plants for food
- Moved according to seasons to find animals and plants
- Lived in family or tribal groups
- Invented tools
- Learned to control and use fire
- Developed language
- Created art

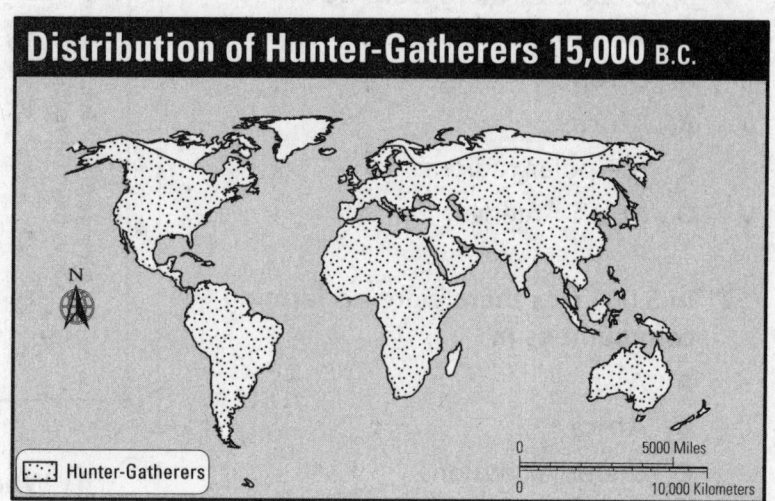

9,000–8,000 B.C.

Farmers

- Domesticated, or tamed, animals
- Learned to grow crops
- Practiced slash-and-burn agriculture
- Built villages

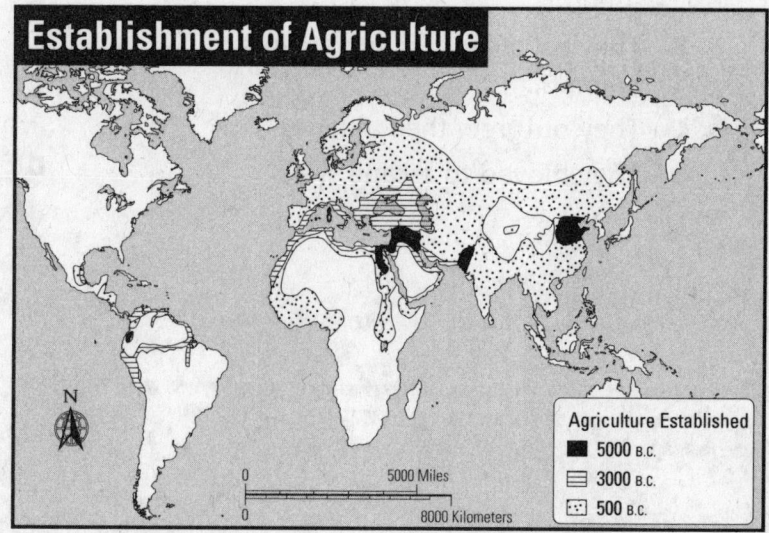

PRACTICE

CALIFORNIA CONTENT STANDARD 6.1

Early Humankind

DIRECTIONS: Choose the letter of the *best* answer.

Use the maps on page 17 to answer questions 1 and 2.

1 In 15,000 B.C., there were no hunter-gatherers in
   A Europe.
   B Africa.
   C the polar regions.
   D North America.

2 In 5,000 B.C., there were no farming communities in
   A Asia.
   B Africa.
   C the polar regions.
   D North America.

3 Why did hunter-gatherers lead nomadic, or traveling, lives?
   A They moved on when the soil was used up.
   B They followed the movements of animals.
   C They outgrew their villages.
   D They moved to escape wars.

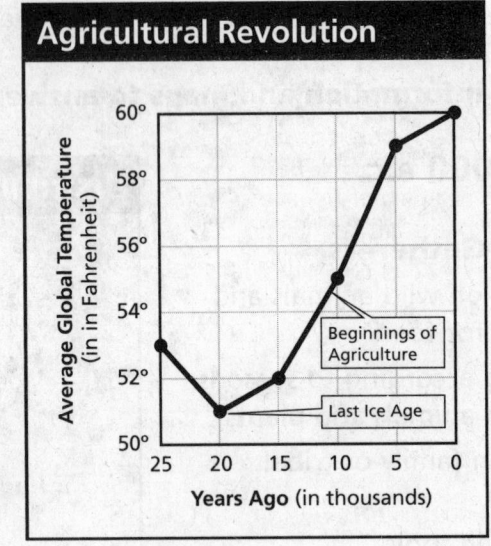

Agricultural Revolution

4 What conclusion about the relationship between agriculture and climate can be drawn from the graph?
   A The development of agriculture produced warmer temperatures.
   B The last Ice Age directly caused the agricultural revolution.
   C Warmer conditions were necessary before agriculture could develop.
   D Agricultural production decreases as temperatures rise.

REVIEW

CALIFORNIA CONTENT
STANDARD 6.2

Ancient River Civilizations
(3500 B.C.–700s B.C.)

OVERALL OBJECTIVE: Analyze the geographic, political, economic, religious, and social structures of the early civilizations of Mesopotamia, Egypt, and Kush.

Read the chart to answer questions on the next page.

	Mesopotamia (Sumer)	Egypt	Kush
Geography	• Flooding of Tigris and Euphrates rivers left fertile soil. • Flooding was unpredictable.	• Flooding of Nile River left fertile soil. • Flooding was predictable.	• A wetter climate allowed agriculture to extend beyond valley of the Nile.
Economy	• farming • trade of surplus (extra) grain in exchange for other resources	• farming and fishing • trade with Africa, Arabia, and Mediterranean	• center of trade network • trade of ivory, animal skins, timber, and minerals • trade along Nile
Government	• Priests, then kings, ruled early city-states. • **Hammurabi's** law code was harsh but protected rights of people.	• Upper and Lower Egypt united around 3000 B.C. • **theocracy:** ruled by a **pharaoh**, or god-king	• Kush conquered Egypt in 700s B.C. • Kush pharaohs ruled.
Culture	• **top:** kings, priests, landowners, officials, merchants • **middle:** farmers and artisans • **bottom:** enslaved people; could not change rank • **women:** landowners, artisans, priestesses, merchants • **writing:** cuneiform, wedge writing	• **top:** pharaoh, priests, nobles, scribes, officials • **middle:** artisans, merchants, farmers • **bottom:** laborers, enslaved people; could change rank • **women:** equal rights • **writing:** hieroglyphics, picture writing	• Egyptian-influenced art and architecture • Egyptian customs, clothing, language, and writing system
Science & Technology	• irrigation • plow and wheel • geometry principles to build irrigation systems	• irrigation • first practical calendar • papyrus • surgery	• smelting iron ore to obtain pure iron
Religion	• many gods • bleak view of death • priests with social power • large temples called ziggurats	• many gods • life after death • priests with social power • pyramids, tombs for afterlife • embalming, preserving bodies for life after death	• Egyptian and Kush gods combined

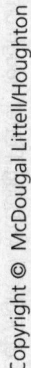

PRACTICE

CALIFORNIA CONTENT
STANDARD 6.2

Ancient River Civilizations
(3500 B.C.–700s B.C.)

DIRECTIONS: Choose the letter of the *best* answer.

1 What effect did the annual flooding of the Tigris and Euphrates rivers have on Mesopotamia?

  A People were forced to move from the rivers to the desert.

  B The flooding made the land useless for agriculture.

  C People were able to farm the land near the rivers.

  D The government put up walls to keep the water away from crops.

2 What was the *most likely* effect of advances such as the plow and improved irrigation on early civilizations?

  A Population decreased.

  B Crop production increased.

  C Villages fought over new technology.

  D More farmers were needed to keep up the supply of food.

3 In Egypt the pharaoh was both the ruler and

  A an emperor.

  B a priest.

  C a commoner.

  D a god.

4 Hammurabi's law code resulted in

  A a more equal system of justice.

  B the removal of the class system.

  C religious freedom for all groups.

  D harsher punishments for crime than ever before in history.

The rulers of ancient Egypt built elaborate tombs filled with gold, jewels, and other treasures for the pharaoh to enjoy in the afterlife.

5 What generalization about the Egyptian civilization can be drawn from the description of the pyramids?

  A Egyptians valued simplicity.

  B Egyptians possessed advanced engineering skills.

  C Egyptians believed in an afterlife.

  D Egyptians had few natural or valuable resources.

6 Which form of writing, practiced by the Sumerians, is described as wedge-shaped?

  A cuneiform

  B glyphs

  C hieroglyphics

  D pictographs

REVIEW

CALIFORNIA CONTENT STANDARD 6.3

The Ancient Hebrews

OVERALL OBJECTIVE: Analyze the geographic, political, economic, religious, and social structures of the Ancient Hebrews.

Read the information to answer questions on the next page.

c. 1800 B.C.—According to tradition, Abraham made a **covenant**, or agreement, with God in which he promised to obey God in return for God's protection of the Hebrews. Abraham's agreement marked beginning of **monotheism**, belief in a single god.

c. 1700 B.C.—During a severe drought, Hebrews went to Egypt.

c. 1250 B.C.—According to tradition, Moses led the Hebrews out of Egypt (an event called the Exodus) and received the **Ten Commandments** from God. The Ten Commandments became the basis for the civil and religious laws of Judaism. These and other laws emphasized equality and the need to live a good life.

c. 1020 B.C.—Saul united the Hebrews and became the first king of Israel.

c. 962 B.C.—King Solomon became king of Israel and built a great temple in Jerusalem.

586 B.C.—Babylonians captured Jerusalem and destroyed the temple. Jews were forced into exile but prophets helped to keep Judaism alive.

515 B.C.—The second temple in Jerusalem was completed.

63 B.C.—Judea was conquered by Romans.

A.D. 70—Romans destroyed the second temple. The **Diaspora** expanded, the forced movement of Jews out of Palestine (Israel). Jews built synagogues (places for prayer and worship) wherever they went.

Sacred Writings of Judaism

Hebrew Bible

- **Torah:** first five books of the Hebrew Bible. Tells the origins of humanity and Judaism.
- **Prophets:** stories about and writings by Jewish prophets.
- **Writings:** collection of poetry, history, stories, and writings.

Talmud

- **Mishnah:** written versions of Jewish oral (or spoken) law.
- **Gemara:** includes explanations and interpretations of the Mishnah.

PRACTICE

CALIFORNIA CONTENT
STANDARD 6.3

The Ancient Hebrews

DIRECTIONS: Choose the letter of the *best* answer.

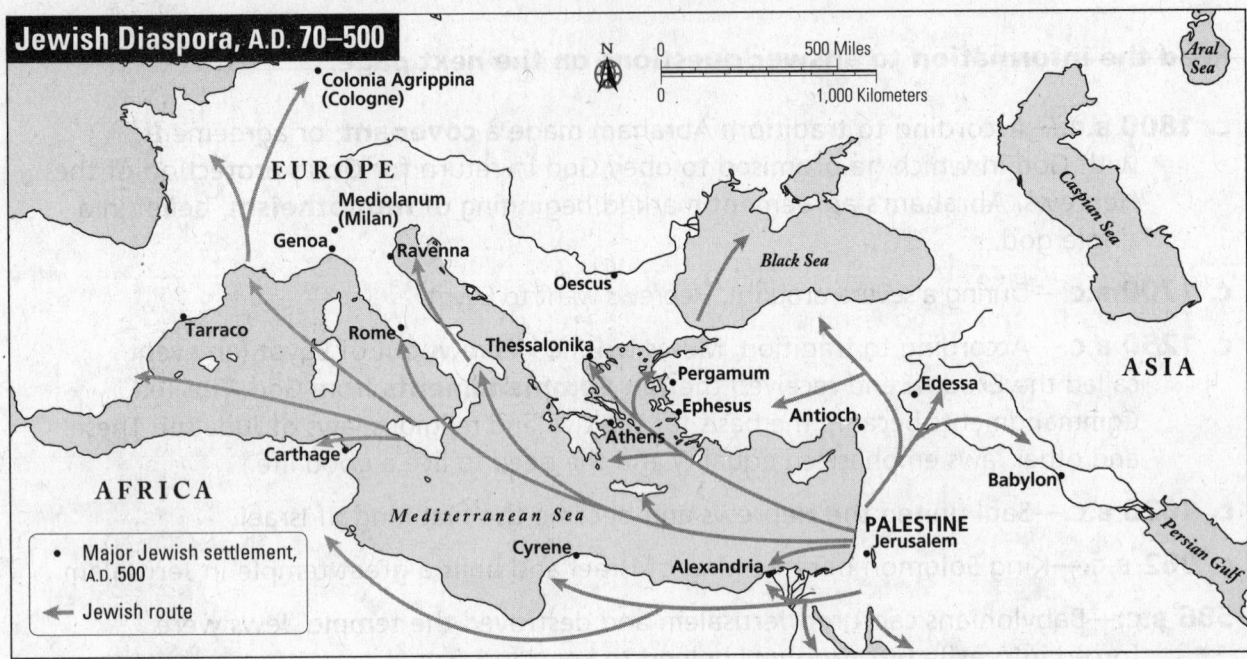

Jewish Diaspora, A.D. 70–500

- • Major Jewish settlement, A.D. 500
- ← Jewish route

1 According to the map, where did most Jews go during the Diaspora?

A Jerusalem

B Aral Sea

C Europe

D Palestine

2 The covenant between Abraham and God established Judaism as a religion

A concerned only with the afterlife.

B in which many gods were worshiped.

C with many strict rules and regulations.

D that focused on the worship of one god.

3 How did ancient Jewish civil and religious laws influence later belief systems and civilizations?

A They were the first written laws.

B They placed emphasis on equality and moral behavior.

C They set a precedent for theocratic government.

D They established the principle of revenge as the proper punishment.

Name _____ Date _____

Ancient Greece

OVERALL OBJECTIVE: Analyze the geographic, political, economic, religious, and social structures of the early civilization of Ancient Greece.

Read the summary to answer questions on the next page.

Geography of Ancient Greece: Rocky land divided by high mountains and deep valleys led to the rise of separate **city-states** rather than one united country. Aegean and Ionian Seas were links that united ancient Greeks for trade.

Greek City-States (700 B.C.–338 B.C.): City-states shared language and beliefs but had different forms of government. By 700 B.C., many were ruled by an **aristocracy**, or group of nobles. Some were controlled by **oligarchies**, in which a group of powerful people ruled. Strong individuals called **tyrants** sometimes seized control, supported by common people.

Athens—A Limited Democracy: Solon opened the assembly to all Athenian citizens. **Cleisthenes** allowed all citizens to submit laws to the assembly for debate. **Pericles** paid public officials so that both rich and poor men could serve if elected. Limited democracy was established in which all free adult male landowners were citizens. All citizens participated directly in the government rather than electing representatives.

Sparta—A Military State: Male citizens entered the army at age 20 and served until they were 60. Enslaved people's labor allowed male citizens to be full-time soldiers. Two kings ruled, and all citizens were part of the assembly.

Persian Wars, 480 B.C.: Sparta, Athens, and other city-states united against the Persians.

Peloponnesian War, 431 B.C.: Under Pericles, Athens took over neighboring city-states. Sparta declared war on Athens. Athens surrendered 27 years later.

Age of Alexander (338 B.C.–330 B.C.): Philip of Macedon conquered the Greek city-states. Philip's son, Alexander, expanded conquests east as far away as India and Egypt. Alexander's armies spread Greek culture wherever they went. Greek culture blended with those of Persia, Egypt, and India to form the Hellenistic culture.

Literature of Ancient Greece: Greek **mythology** explained the world around them and told stories about Greek gods and goddesses. Greeks composed **epic poems**, such as the *Iliad* and the *Odyssey*, about their heroes. **Aesop** and others wrote fables, stories involving animals that teach a moral lesson.

Name _____   Date _____

Ancient Greece

DIRECTIONS: Choose the letter of the *best* answer.

1 What geographical circumstance *most likely* led to the development of city-states in ancient Greece?

   A the fact that it is mostly flat

   B its closeness to Asia

   C an absence of rivers or coastlines

   D its division into separate regions by mountains

2 Which sequence identifies the evolution of government in Athens?

   A tyranny to oligarchy to democracy

   B oligarchy to aristocracy to democracy

   C dictatorship to democracy to oligarchy

   D aristocracy to tyranny to democracy

3 A direct democracy is one in which

   A representatives are elected by the people to make laws.

   B all citizens participate in the law-making and governing process.

   C a few powerful leaders are voted in by the people.

   D an electoral college elects a president.

4 In what way were Athens and Sparta similar?

   A They were both democracies.

   B They were both military states.

   C They were both on the same side in the Peloponnesian War.

   D They both resisted Persian advances into Greece.

5 What was *one* result of Alexander's conquest of the Mediterranean world?

   A the collapse of Greek civilization

   B the rise of the Roman culture

   C the development of democratic practices in all Greek city-states

   D the spread of Greek culture to distant lands

6 Like the ancient Greeks, people of today turn to Aesop's fables to

   A find out about the Greek gods.

   B identify the traits of Greek heroes.

   C trace important events in Greek history.

   D learn lessons about how to live their lives well.

Name _____   Date _____

REVIEW

CALIFORNIA CONTENT
STANDARD 6.5

Early Civilizations of India

OVERALL OBJECTIVE: Analyze the geographic, political, economic, religious, and social structures of the early civilizations of India.

Read the summary to answer questions on the next page.

Indian Civilization

The Caste System When the Aryans migrated into India in 1500 B.C., their class system consisted of three groups: warriors, priests, and commoners. Later this became a more rigid and complicated caste system. People were born into a caste for life. Their caste system determined how they interacted with other people, the people they could marry, and what kinds of jobs they held. It also limited contact with non-Aryans.

Achievements in the Arts and Sciences The arts and sciences flourished under the Aryans. The rich literature heritage of Sanskrit, an ancient language of India, includes the *Bhagavad Gita,* a sacred text about the warrior Prince Arjuna.

Indian mathematicians were highly advanced. They invented the Hindu-Arabic numeral system, the decimal system, and the zero (which was also invented independently by the Maya). They also identified the value of *pi* as the circumference of a circle divided by its diameter.

The Rise of Buddhism (528 B.C.) One of the greatest contributions of early Indian civilization is Buddhism. Siddhartha Gautama, a Hindu prince, spent several years searching for a way to escape suffering in life. Finally he meditated for 49 days under a large fig tree and received insight. He became the Buddha, the enlightened. Buddhism is based on the **Four Noble Truths:**

- People suffer because their minds are not at ease.
- Suffering comes from wanting what one does not have.
- People can stop suffering by not wanting.
- People can stop wanting by following the Eightfold Path, which outlines the right way to live. This leads to nirvana, or the end of suffering.

Buddhist teaching includes the belief in nonviolence and reincarnation, as well as rejection of the caste system and the worship of Hindu deities.

Buddhism spread throughout India, supported by Buddhist rulers. In the seventh century, Buddhism in India almost disappeared. It remained strong in other countries of Asia, where it was brought by traders and missionaries.

Name _____ Date _____

DIRECTIONS: Choose the letter of the *best* answer.

Use the diagram to answer questions 1 and 2.

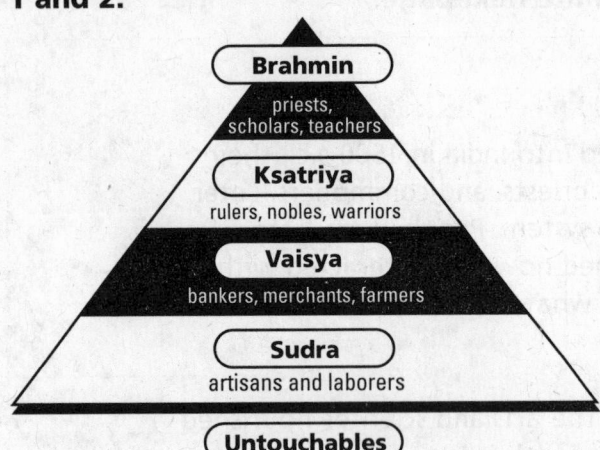

1 Based on the diagram, what did Indian society value the most?

  A wealth

  B noble birth

  C creativity

  D knowledge

2 What was *most likely* the kind of job performed by the Untouchables?

  A jobs requiring skill and education

  B jobs too lowly for others to want

  C jobs involving exchange of money

  D jobs that needed training

3 The Eightfold Path guides Buddhists to

  A heaven.

  B nirvana.

  C the Four Noble Truths.

  D reincarnation.

4 How did Buddhism mainly spread to other countries in Asia?

  A The Buddha traveled and preached widely outside of India.

  B Rulers used military force to impose Buddhism on conquered peoples.

  C Traders and missionaries carried Buddhism to other countries.

  D People received favored status if they converted to Buddhism.

5 What was invented by Indian mathematicians?

  A zero and Hindu-Arabic numerals

  B abacus and zero

  C geometry and the abacus

  D algebra and the value of pi

"Send thy [your] most excellent beams to shine and light us, ... Granting us food. . . ."

—the *Rig Veda*, translated by Nicol Macnicol.

6 According to the quotation, why did the Aryans pray to the deity Dawn?

  A for adequate rainfall

  B for the arrival of each day

  C for the sunlight to grow crops

  D for salvation

Name _____ Date _____

Early Civilizations of China

OVERALL OBJECTIVE: Analyze the geographic, political, economic, religious, and social structures of the early civilizations of China.

Read the chart to answer questions on the next page.

551 B.C. Birth of Confucius	**Confucius** • Taught a code of proper conduct. • Identified five important relationships: ruler/subject; father/son; husband/wife; brothers; friends. • Believed social order, harmony, and good government should be based on family relationships.	• Taught that rulers and subjects should respect each other and that people should respect their parents and elders. • Stressed education. • Set clear family and social roles to help avoid conflict.
c. 500s B.C. Life of Laozi	**Laozi** • Taught that a universal force called the **Dao** guides all things. • Searched for knowledge and understanding through nature. • Believed natural order is more important than social order.	• Stressed the importance of living simply and in harmony with nature. • Laid the foundation for many advances in astronomy, alchemy, and medicine.
221 B.C. Beginning of Qin Dynasty under Shi Huangdi	**Shi Huangdi** • Unified and expanded China during Qin Dynasty. • Ruled harshly. • Used peasant labor to build roads to keep empire unified.	• Instituted government standards for weights, measures, coins, and writing. • Began building the Great Wall to keep out northern invaders.
202 B.C. Beginning of Han Dynasty	**The Han** • Developed a large government bureaucracy. • Instituted a state exam, testing knowledge of Confucianism, for government positions. • Expanded China's borders to include northern Vietnam, northern Korea, and southern provinces.	• Sent paper, silk, and pottery to the west along the Silk Roads in exchange for sesame seeds, metals, and precious stones. • Were influenced by ideas, such as Buddhism, through interaction along the Silk Roads.

Name _____   Date _____

PRACTICE

Early Civilizations of China

DIRECTIONS: Choose the letter of the *best* answer.

1 A basic difference between the philosophy of Confucius and that of Laozi is that Laozi

   A believed in the importance of social relationships.

   B stressed the need to gain material wealth.

   C urged his followers to be guided by nature.

   D wanted the government to play a greater role in people's lives.

2 What *most likely* resulted from the Han use of a state exam to select government officials?

   A The bureaucracy decreased in size.

   B Favored nobles received positions.

   C More qualified applicants received government jobs.

   D Corruption within the government increased.

3 What did China receive from trade along the Silk Roads?

   A silk and paper

   B Daoism and hemp fiber

   C metals and precious stones

   D pottery and paper

4 How did Buddhism come to China?

   A Buddhism originated from the teachings of Shi Huangdi.

   B Chinese traders were exposed to Buddhism along the Silk Roads.

   C Buddhism was taught by Confucius.

   D Northern Korea introduced China to Buddhism during the Han Dynasty.

Name _____ Date _____

The Roman Republic

OVERALL OBJECTIVE: Analyze the geographic, political, economic, religious, and social structures during the development of Rome.

Read the summary to answer questions on the next page.

The Founding of Rome, 753 B.C.: According to legend, Romulus founded Rome near the Tiber River. The early Romans were ruled by Etruscan kings. In 509 B.C., the Romans overthrew the Etruscan rule and founded a republic.

The Roman Republic: The new republic consisted of the powerful **patricians**, or nobles, and the **plebeians**, or common people. In time, the plebeians won the right to elect representatives called tribunes. They also had their own assembly. The **Twelve Tables**, the law code written in 451 B.C. protected the rights of all citizens.

Three Branches of Government:

- **Executive Branch**—Two **consuls** were elected for one year. They were chief executives of the government and commanders-in-chief of the military.
- **Legislative Branch**—A **senate** of 300 was chosen from the aristocracy.
- **Judicial Branch**—Eight judges, or praetors, were chosen for one year.

End of the Republic, 46 B.C.: During a civil war, **Julius Caesar**, a Roman general, won great popularity among the people. He ended the war and was named **dictator** for life. He was an absolute ruler, expanded the senate, enforced laws against crime, and created jobs for the poor. He was assassinated by senators who feared his growing power.

The Roman Empire, 27 B.C.: Caesar's great nephew, **Augustus**, became Rome's first emperor. Augustus had absolute power but retained the senate, consuls, and tribunes. Under his rule, Rome expanded and enjoyed a period of peace and prosperity.

The Roots of Christianity, A.D. 6: The Romans made the Jewish kingdom of Judea, Jesus's birthplace, a Roman province. Both a Jew and a Roman subject, Jesus preached justice and compassion. Jesus's success and popularity made enemies of the Roman officials. As a result, he was put to death. After Jesus's death, his **disciples,** or followers, continued preaching his message.

Name _____   Date _____

DIRECTIONS: Choose the letter of the *best* answer.

1 Which event marked the beginning of the Roman Republic?

 A the assassination of Julius Caesar

 B the overthrow of Etruscan rule

 C established the Twelve Tables

 D the rise of Augustus

2 Why was the consuls' term of office limited to one year?

 A to allow as many people as possible to be consuls

 B to prevent them from gaining too much power

 C because the first consuls only served a year

 D because the consuls then became the commanders-in-chief of the army

3 In what way were Augustus and Julius Caesar similar?

 A Both upheld republican ideals.

 B Both held the title of emperor.

 C Both had absolute power.

 D Both expanded the government.

Use the chart below to answer question 4.

4 Based on the chart, what are some contributions of the Roman Empire to future civilizations?

 A architecture, language, law, religion

 B technology, law, mathematics

 C architecture, medicine, law, language

 D language, astronomy, art, medicine

Legacies of Ancient Rome			
The Arts	**Technology**	**Government**	**Culture**
• Epic poetry • Arch and dome • Mosaics and frescoes • Sculpture	• Use of concrete in engineering • System of roads • Aqueducts	• Legal systems • Republican forms	• Spread of Christianity • Influence of Latin on Romance languages

Name _____ Date _____

CALIFORNIA CONTENT STANDARD 7.1.1

Rome's Decline and Lasting Legacy

SPECIFIC OBJECTIVE: Study the early strengths and lasting contributions of Rome and its ultimate internal weaknesses.

Read the summary to answer questions on the next page.

Decline of the Roman Empire

- By the second century, the Roman Empire had stopped expanding. Taxes were raised, causing economic hardship for many citizens.
- Fewer people could afford the cost of education and communication in the empire broke down. This led to an uninvolved and ignorant population.
- Agriculture declined. Soil had become exhausted. Because slave labor was used, farmers had little reason to try helpful new technologies.
- Hunger and disease, brought on by the poor harvests, reduced the population.
- Soldiers became less disciplined. Their loyalty to the emperor decreased.
- Roman politicians became corrupt, entering public office only for financial gain.

Rome's Downfall

- A Germanic tribe took advantage of Rome's weakness and invaded in A.D. 476.
- The Franks conquered the rest of the Roman Empire in France and Switzerland.

The Legacy of Rome

- **Art:** Romans made mosaic popular. Mosaic is a kind of floor or wall art made of tiny pieces of tile or glass. Romans also preserved realistic Greek sculpture.
- **Philosophy:** The Greek philosophy of stoicism influenced Roman thought. Stoicism shaped ideas of citizenship stressing virtue and duty.
- **Language:** Latin is the basis for Spanish, Italian, French, Portuguese, and Romanian—the Romance languages. Many English words have Latin roots.
- **Architecture and Engineering:** The Romans used arches, domes, and vaults to create large, impressive buildings. Arches were also used to construct aqueducts that brought fresh water into cities. Romans developed a system of roads totaling more than 50,000 miles.
- **Religion:** Later rulers made Christianity the official religion of the empire. Eventually, Christianity spread throughout the western world.
- **Law and Government:** Rome's system guaranteed equal treatment under the law. People were innocent until proven guilty. The Roman senate and assembly became models for later democracies.

Name _____   Date _____

Rome's Decline and Lasting Legacy

DIRECTIONS: Choose the letter of the *best* answer.

1 **Which of the following statements about the decline of Rome is *true*?**

A Economic decline resulted from increased taxes.

B A lack of communication resulted in a disinterested population.

C As a result of slave labor, the soil became highly productive.

D Hunger and disease weakened the military.

2 **Why was the military less effective after the second century?**

A The draft ended, and fewer men wanted to be soldiers.

B The army was scattered across a very wide area.

C The troops were needed to maintain control in newly conquered territories.

D Soldiers no longer were loyal to the emperor.

3 **An important principle of Roman law was that**

A citizens had freedom of speech.

B property could not be taken without just cause.

C all citizens had freedom of religion.

D a person was innocent until proven guilty.

The masterpiece of the building is one of the largest domes made of stone and concrete ever built. It covers a circular chamber, or rotunda, that is proportioned like a perfect sphere. . .

4 **Based on the passage describing the building of a temple to the Roman gods, what inference might be made?**

A Roman engineers knew geometry.

B The Romans only constructed domes for temples.

C The technology of building domes was lost when the Roman Empire fell.

D Many workers most likely lost their lives while trying to build the temple.

Name _____ Date _____

The Height of the Roman Empire (27 B.C.–A.D. 180)

SPECIFIC OBJECTIVE: Discuss the geographic borders of the Roman Empire at its height and the factors that threatened it.

Study the map and summary to answer questions on the next page.

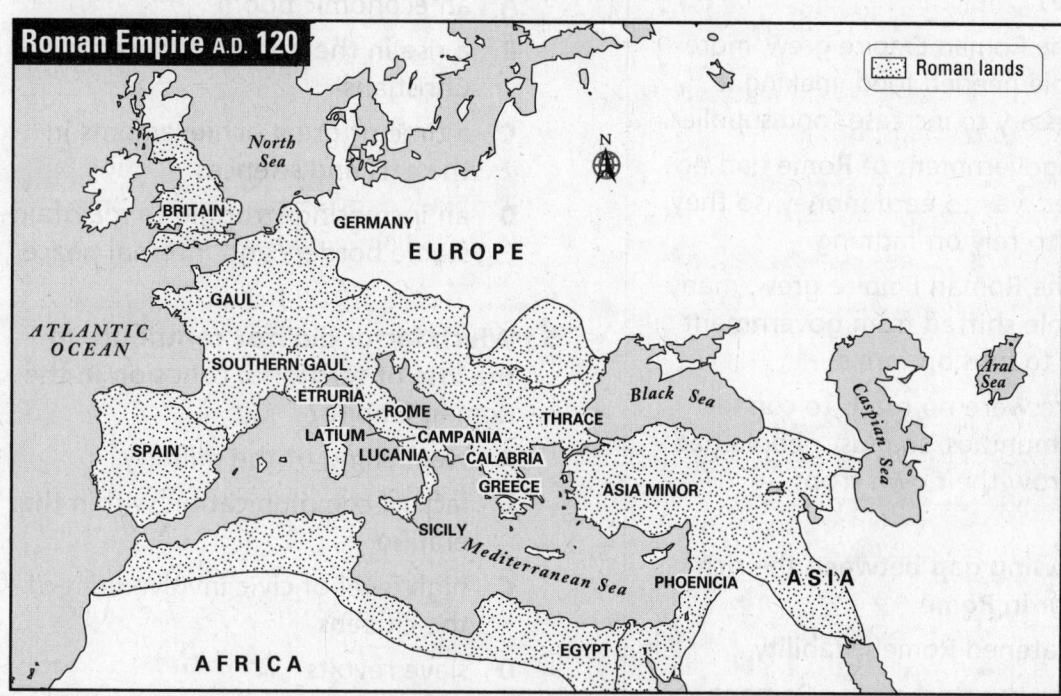

Roman Empire A.D. 120

Factors Helping Rome's Expansion

- *Pax Romana*, a period of peace and prosperity that lasted for over 200 years
- Strong rulers, beginning with the first emperor Augustus who built a strong and stable government
- Efficient bureaucracy run by civil servants who managed tax collection, grain distribution, and the postal system
- Thriving agriculture
- Extensive trade network
- Powerful army and navy
- Stable borders
- Vast network of roads connecting parts of the empire

Factors Threatening the Roman Empire (after A.D. 180)

- End of *Pax Romana*
- Growing gap between the rich and the poor
- Slave revolts
- Initial rise of Christianity
- Economic problems, including inflation, bad harvests, and loss of revenue
- Disruption of trade by pirates
- Weakening of the military
- Indifference and ignorance of citizenry
- Continued threat of invasion from Germanic and other tribes

Name _____ Date _____

DIRECTIONS: Choose the letter of the *best* answer.

1 Why was a thriving agricultural system important to the expansion of Rome?

  A As the Roman Empire grew, more people needed food, making it necessary to increase food supplies.

  B The government of Rome had no other way to earn money, so they had to rely on farming.

  C As the Roman Empire grew, many people shifted from government jobs to jobs on farms.

  D There were no roads to connect communities, so most people had to grow their own crops.

2 The growing gap between the rich and poor in Rome

  A threatened Rome's stability.

  B led to the start of *Pax Romana.*

  C had little effect on the empire.

  D was the direct result of the policies of Augustus.

Use the map on page 33 to answer question 3.

3 At its height, the Roman Empire included

  A most of Africa, Asia, and Europe.

  B western Europe and the Mediterranean regions.

  C Germany and nearby regions.

  D the regions east of the Caspian Sea.

4 What did the end of *Pax Romana* mean for the empire?

  A an economic boom

  B a rise in the number of practicing Christians

  C a time of great achievements in the arts and sciences

  D an increasing struggle to maintain stable borders and internal peace

5 Which factor did *not* contribute to the loss of territorial cohesion in the Roman Empire?

  A weakening of the military

  B lack of communication within the empire

  C high level of civic involvement of the citizens

  D slave revolts

6 The civil service system in Rome

  A provided efficiency and continuity in the government.

  B increased corruption among officials.

  C promoted rivalry between patricians and plebeians over government jobs.

  D moved the empire toward more democratic forms of government.

REVIEW

CALIFORNIA CONTENT STANDARD 7.1.3

The Byzantine Empire

SPECIFIC OBJECTIVE: Describe the establishment of Constantinople and the development of the Byzantine Empire, with an emphasis on the differences between the Eastern Orthodox and Roman Catholic civilizations.

Read the chart to answer questions on the next page.

A.D. 330	Emperor Constantine moved the capital of the Roman Empire to Byzantium in the eastern part of the empire. The city became known as Constantinople.
A.D. 395	Continuing problems forced Roman leaders to divide the empire into two: the Western Roman Empire and the Byzantine Empire.
A.D. 476	The Western Roman Empire fell to Germanic invaders. The Byzantine Empire survived.
A.D. 527–565	Under Justinian I, the Byzantine Empire included many lands once in the Roman Empire. Justinian I also developed a law code, which was used for the next 900 years. Constantinople's walls were strengthened, and new buildings, such as the Hagia Sophia, a huge church, were constructed. Justinian I helped to preserve Greco-Roman culture.
A.D. 730	Emperor Leo III stopped the use of icons, religious images used to help people worship. The pope in Rome sided with those who supported the use of icons. The controversy highlighted the differences between the Eastern and Western churches.
A.D. 843	Empress Theodora brought back the use of icons in Eastern churches.
A.D. 1054	The Church split into the Roman Catholic Church in the West and the Orthodox Church in the East. This happened after an argument between the pope and the head of the Eastern Church, the patriarch. Both churches continued to base their faith on the gospels and Bible, celebrate the sacraments, and try to convert new believers. The Roman Catholic Church, however, recognized the pope as the head of the church, conducted services in Latin, and did not allow priests to marry. The Eastern Orthodox Church conducted services, recognized the authority of the emperor over religious leaders, and allowed priests to marry.
A.D. 1453	Constantinople fell.

PRACTICE

CALIFORNIA CONTENT
STANDARD 7.1.3

The Byzantine Empire

DIRECTIONS: Choose the letter of the *best* answer.

Use the map to answer questions 1 and 2.

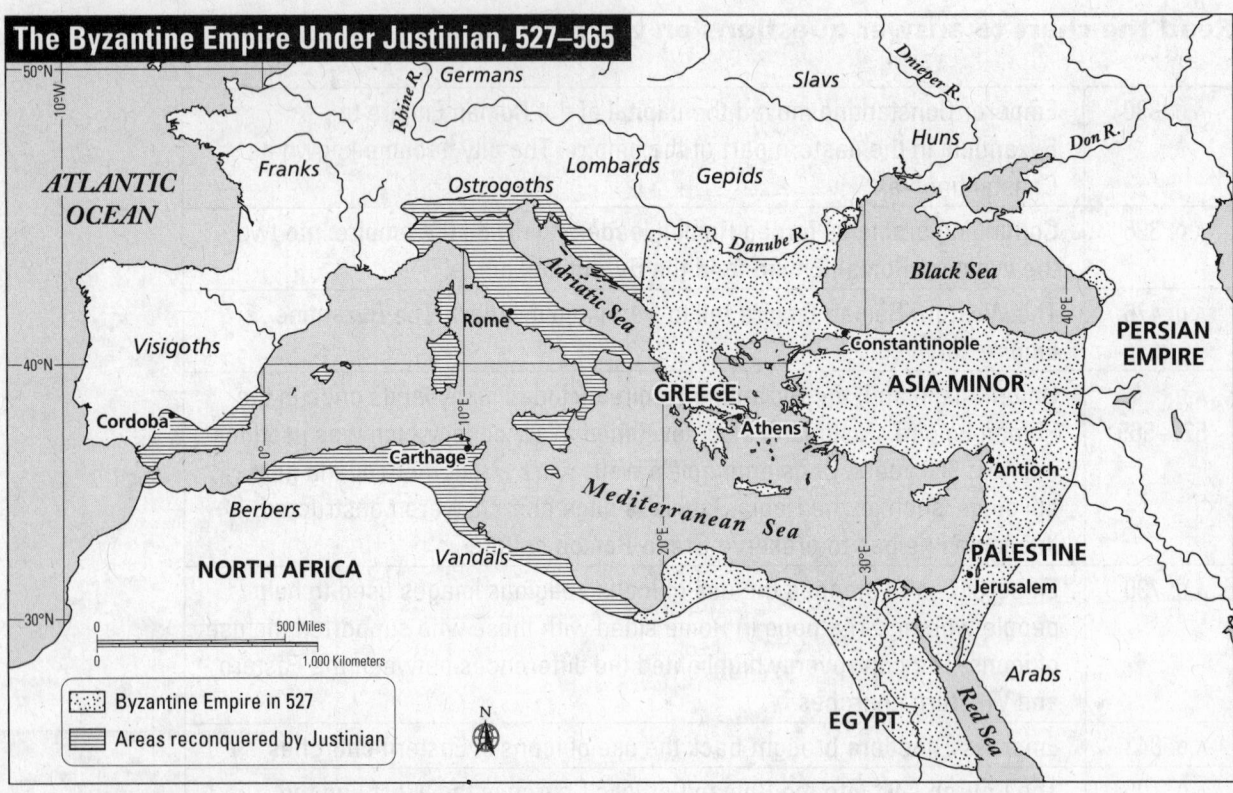

The Byzantine Empire Under Justinian, 527–565

1 **According to the map, which of the following statements about the Byzantine Empire under Justinian is accurate?**

A Justinian reconquered many of the areas held by the Franks.

B Under Justinian, the Byzantine Empire grew larger.

C Justinian kept the borders of the Byzantine Empire stable.

D Justinian reduced the size of the Byzantine Empire.

2 **As shown on the map, Constantinople's location**

A meant it could not be reached by traders.

B was impossible to defend from attacks by land.

C was on major trade routes between Europe and Asia.

D had no effect on its military or economic situation.

Arshawn
Puaar
6°

REVIEW

CALIFORNIA CONTENT STANDARD 7.2.1

The Arabian Peninsula

SPECIFIC OBJECTIVE: Identify the physical features and describe the climate of the Arabian peninsula, its relationship to surrounding bodies of land and water, and nomadic and sedentary ways of life.

Read the summary to answer questions on the next page.

The Geography of the Arabian Peninsula

The Arabian Peninsula stretches 1,200 miles from north to south and 1,300 miles from east to west. It is strategically located at a crossroads of three continents—Africa, Europe, and Asia. It is surrounded by bodies of water including the Mediterranean Sea, the Red Sea, the Arabian Sea, and the Persian Gulf.

Yet the Arabian Peninsula is covered mostly by desert, and the climate is arid. There are some oases in the desert, but farmland is extremely limited. Most farming is done on a strip of land along the northern coastline and an area in the southern mountains.

The Effects of Geography

The Arabian Peninsula can support little agriculture. Bedouins led a nomadic existence, moving from oasis to oasis to find pasture for their flocks. As a way to survive the harshness of their environment, Bedouins organized themselves into self-governing clans, families related by blood or marriage. They developed fighting skills defending their water or grazing rights against other clans. Some Bedouins settled at oases. An extensive trade network gradually grew between Bedouins, trading centers at the oases, and cities in Asia, Africa, and the Byzantine Empire.

PRACTICE

CALIFORNIA CONTENT
STANDARD 7.2.1

The Arabian Peninsula

DIRECTIONS: Choose the letter of the *best* answer.

1 The Arabian Peninsula is mostly

  A tundra.

  B desert.

  C rainforest.

  D grasslands.

2 Why were the Bedouins nomads?

  A Hostile invaders kept them constantly on the move.

  B They were hunters and followed animals from place to place.

  C They moved from oasis to oasis in search of grazing lands for their herds.

  D They relocated when the farmland could no longer support them.

3 How did the Bedouins develop military skills?

  A Every man had to serve in the military for a certain number of years.

  B Piracy was one of the ways in which they made their living.

  C They often had to fight against other clans to protect their water and grazing rights.

  D The natural resources of the Arabian Peninsula were highly sought after.

4 Which geographical factor contributed *most* to the development of trade between the Arabian Peninsula and regions in Africa, Asia, and the Byzantine Empire?

  A the peninsula's location

  B its dry climate

  C the size of the peninsula

  D the scarcity of farmland

5 In what way did trade affect settlements at the oases?

  A The settlements grew into large cities.

  B They became military bases.

  C Trade largely passed through the oasis settlements.

  D The population decreased as many people relocated to other regions.

5/5

Name _____ Date _____

CALIFORNIA CONTENT STANDARD 7.2.2

Origins of Islam

SPECIFIC OBJECTIVE: Trace the origins of Islam and the life and teachings of Muhammad, including Islamic teachings on the connection with Judaism and Christianity.

Read the summary to answer questions on the next page.

The Life of Muhammad (570–632)

Muhammad was about 40 when he began experiencing visits from the angel Gabriel. He passed the revelations, or messages, on to his followers. One of his most important teachings was that there was only one God, Allah. This was the beginning of the religion known as Islam. Those who followed its teachings became known as Muslims, those who have submitted to the will of Allah.

Mecca, where Muhammad began his public teaching, was already a holy site. It contained the Ka'aba, a shrine associated with Abraham. Muhammad's ideas were not accepted in Mecca. He and his followers had to flee to Yathrib, later called Medina. This journey is known as the Hijrah. In Medina, Muhammad achieved success. He became the political, military, and religious leader of the community of Arabs, Jews, and Muslims. In 603, he led 10,000 followers back to Mecca, which surrendered without a fight.

The Islamic Faith

Islam teaches that there is only one God, Allah. Every person is responsible for choosing between good and evil. Muslims' duties are known as the **Five Pillars of Islam:**

- Muslims must testify to the belief in one God through a statement of faith.
- Muslims must pray in the direction of Mecca five times a day.
- Muslims must pay a religious tax to support the less fortunate.
- Muslims must fast during the day in the holy month of Ramadan.
- Muslims must make a pilgrimage to Mecca (a hajj) if they are able.

Islam's Relationship to Judaism and Christianity

Muslims believe that Allah is the same God that is worshiped by Jews and Christians. They believe, however, that Jesus is a prophet rather than the Son of God. Muslims believe that the Qur'an, the Torah, and the Bible all contain the word of God, but that the Qur'an is the perfected version. All three religions believe in heaven and hell and a day of judgment. Muslims, Jews, and Christians believe they are descended from Abraham.

PRACTICE

CALIFORNIA CONTENT
STANDARD 7.2.2

Origins of Islam

DIRECTIONS: Choose the letter of the *best* answer.

I	Hijrah to Medina
II	First revelations from the angel Gabriel to Muhammad
III	Surrender of Mecca to Muhammad's followers
IV	Muhammad's persecution in Mecca

1 In what order did the significant events in Muhammad's life, as shown in the box, occur?

A III, IV, I, II

B I, II, III, IV

C II, IV, I, III

D IV, II, IV, I

2 Muhammad's followers were called Muslims because they

A came from Mecca.

B believed in Muhammad as a prophet.

C accepted the will of God.

D no longer worshiped many gods.

3 What happened after the Hijrah?

A Muhammad moved to Baghdad.

B Muhammad and his followers won their first battle.

C Muhammad encountered his first opposition.

D Muhammad became a political and religious leader in Medina.

4 Why do Muslims pray in the direction of Mecca?

A It is in the center of the Arabian Peninsula.

B It was from a shrine in Mecca that the Muslim faithful were first called to pray.

C It symbolizes the hardships that the faithful must endure for their faith.

D It is in the direction that the sun sets.

5 What are *two* important teachings that are common to Islam, Judaism, and Christianity?

A dietary laws and belief in one God

B Judgment Day and abstinence from alcohol

C life after death and Judgment Day

D descent from Abraham and observation of a month of fasting

6 What is the relationship among the Torah, the Bible, and Qur'an according to Muslims?

A They are the same, only written in different languages.

B The Qur'an continues the story begun first in the Torah and then in the Bible.

C The Bible includes the Torah and the Qur'an.

D They are all holy books that contain sacred revelations.

REVIEW

CALIFORNIA CONTENT STANDARD 7.2.3

The Qur'an and the Sunnah

SPECIFIC OBJECTIVE: Explain the significance of the Qur'an and the Sunnah as the primary sources of Islamic beliefs, practice, and law, and their influence in Muslims' daily life.

Read the chart to answer questions on the next page.

The Qur'an

The Qur'an is the Muslim holy book. It contains the speech of God delivered to Muhammad by the angel Gabriel over a period of 20 years. It is divided into 114 surahs, or chapters. It is said that each time Muhammad received the revelations, he was in a trance. Upon awakening, he would speak the words, which were then memorized or written down by his listeners. After Muhammad's death, all the revelations were collected. Eventually, a final version of the Qur'an was recorded.

The Qur'an is seen by Muslims as infallible, or correct, in all matters. It is the final authority. The revelations received first at Mecca relate to spiritual and ethical matters. They also refer to the Day of Judgment. The later revelations focus on the organization and laws of the Islamic community.

Shari`ah

The shari`ah refers to the laws that regulate Muslims' lives. The most important source for these laws is the Qur'an, the primary guide for Muslims. The Sunnah is the second source of Islamic law. The shari`ah covers spiritual matters and behavior and manners. It also includes international law and laws pertaining to family, business, government, and punishments for crime.

The Sunnah

Sunnah means "habitual practice" in Arabic. In other words, it refers to the practices and customs of Muslims. These traditions were established by the words and actions of Muhammad. These words and actions are recorded in the Hadith.

The Sunnah is used to help make decisions about matters not covered in the Qur'an.

PRACTICE

CALIFORNIA CONTENT
STANDARD 7.2.3

The Qur'an and the Sunnah

DIRECTIONS: Choose the letter of the *best* answer.

1 **Which statement about the origin of the Qur'an is correct?**

A The Qur'an was written by Muhammad after his first visit from the angel.

B The oral and written revelations of Muhammad were collected into the Qur'an after his death.

C The Qur'an is an oral account of Muhammad's teachings.

D Muhammad kept a written account of all of his revelations.

2 **What is the attitude of Muslims toward the teachings contained in the Qur'an?**

A The teachings are open to interpretation.

B The Qur'an may be used to support Muslims' own opinions.

C The teachings in the Qur'an are always correct.

D Some of the teachings are outdated.

3 **What is the significance of the Qur'an to Muslims?**

A The Qur'an is sometimes referred to in spiritual arguments.

B The Qur'an is the major influence on Muslims' lives.

C The Qur'an is seen primarily as a great work of literature.

D The Qur'an is reserved for religious rituals.

4 **What is the importance of the Sunnah?**

A It contains the Islamic dietary restrictions.

B It shows Muslims how to live their faith through Muhammad's example.

C It contains the revelations sent from God through Gabriel.

D It records the early history of Islam, written by Muhammad.

_____

"To the men a share from what they have earned, and to the women a share from what they have earned."

—from *The Koran Interpreted*,
translated by Arthur J. Arberry
_____

5 **In the quotation, what is the Qur'an saying about the rights of women?**

A Women cannot inherit property.

B Women are dependent upon their husbands for all of their needs.

C Women are entitled to own property and earn a living.

D Women are required to remove themselves from society.

Name _____   Date _____

CALIFORNIA CONTENT
STANDARD 7.2.4   *Spread of Islam*

SPECIFIC OBJECTIVE: Discuss the expansion of Muslim rule, emphasizing
Muslim civilization and the spread of Islam and the Arabic language.

Read the information to answer questions on the next page.

A.D. 632	Abu-Bakr became the first caliph, "successor," to Muhammad. When rebellion among some Muslims broke out, Abu Bakr used military force to put down the rebellion, control central Arabia, and conquer lands to the north.
A.D. 644–661	During this period the Muslims were led by Abu-Bakr, Umar, Uthmar, and Ali. The first four caliphs conquered Southwest Asia and parts of North Africa. Using force and treaties, they expanded the empire fourfold. They allowed freedom of religion, although non-Muslims paid a special tax. Jews and Christians were given a special status and held roles in the government. Many people in the territories ruled by the Muslims converted to Islam. They were attracted by the message of equality and hope for salvation.
A.D. 661–750	The Umayyad dynasty began after the last of the first four caliphs was killed. This led to a split in Islam. Some did not accept the rule of the Umayyads. They believed the caliph should be related to Muhammad. They were called Shiites. Those who accepted the Umayyads were called Sunnis and followed the Sunnah or Muhammad's example. Under Umayyad rule, the capital moved from Medina to Damascus. The empire grew to include North Africa, the Iberian Peninsula, and much of Central Asia. To unify their empire, the Umayyads developed a bureaucracy and appointed governors to rule provinces. They used a common currency and made Arabic the official government language.
A.D. 750	The Abbasid caliphate began. To keep control, the Abbasids built a huge standing army. They promoted a policy of inclusion, in which all Muslims, whether Arab or non-Arab, were equal, and encouraged Christians and Jews to serve in the government. They moved the capital to Baghdad.
A.D. 756	The Umayyad Abd al-Rahman escaped the killing of the Umayyads by the Abbasids. He fled to Spain and established Umayyad rule, laying the foundation for the Umayyad caliphate. Later leaders added to the territory of Al-Andalus.
A.D. 909–1171	The Fatimids, a group that opposed the Abbasids, drove them out of the area of Egypt and Tunisia and set up their own caliphate.
A.D. 1258	The caliphate ended when the Mongols invaded and killed the caliph.

Name _____   Date _____

DIRECTIONS: Choose the letter of the *best* answer.

1 In what way were the Sunnis different from the Shiites?

  A The Sunnis believed in Christianity.

  B The Sunnis did not want the capital to move from Medina to Damascus.

  C The Sunnis accepted the rule of the Umayyads.

  D The Sunnis believed that the caliph should be related to Muhammad.

2 Which of the following events happened *after* the Abbasids were driven out of Egypt and Tunisia?

  A Abd al-Rahman established Umayyad rule in Spain.

  B The Fatimids set up their caliphate.

  C The Abbasids moved the capital to Baghdad.

  D Abu-Bakr succeeded Muhammad.

3 How did the various groups of Muslims expand the empire through the years?

  A They made treaties with neighboring regions.

  B They used military tactics.

  C They made alliances and conquered by force.

  D They flooded new regions with large numbers of Muslims.

4 What most likely resulted from the policy of inclusion under the Abbasids?

  A Unfriendliness between Arab and non-Arab Muslims decreased.

  B Jewish government officials lost their positions.

  C More religions were practiced in the empire.

  D Fewer Arabs converted to Islam.

5 Which of the following was a method used by the Umayyads to unify their empire?

  A military rule

  B official use of Arabic

  C forced conversion to Islam

  D a system of roads and canals

6 How were conquered people treated within the Muslim Empire?

  A They were enslaved.

  B They were forced to give up their religion and convert to Islam.

  C Their religions were tolerated, but some taxes were imposed.

  D They were moved to the least desirable parts of the region.

Name _____ Date _____

CALIFORNIA CONTENT STANDARD 7.2.5

Trade in the Arab World

SPECIFIC OBJECTIVE: Describe the growth of cities and the establishment of trade routes among Asia, Africa, and Europe.

Study the map and summary to answer questions on the next page.

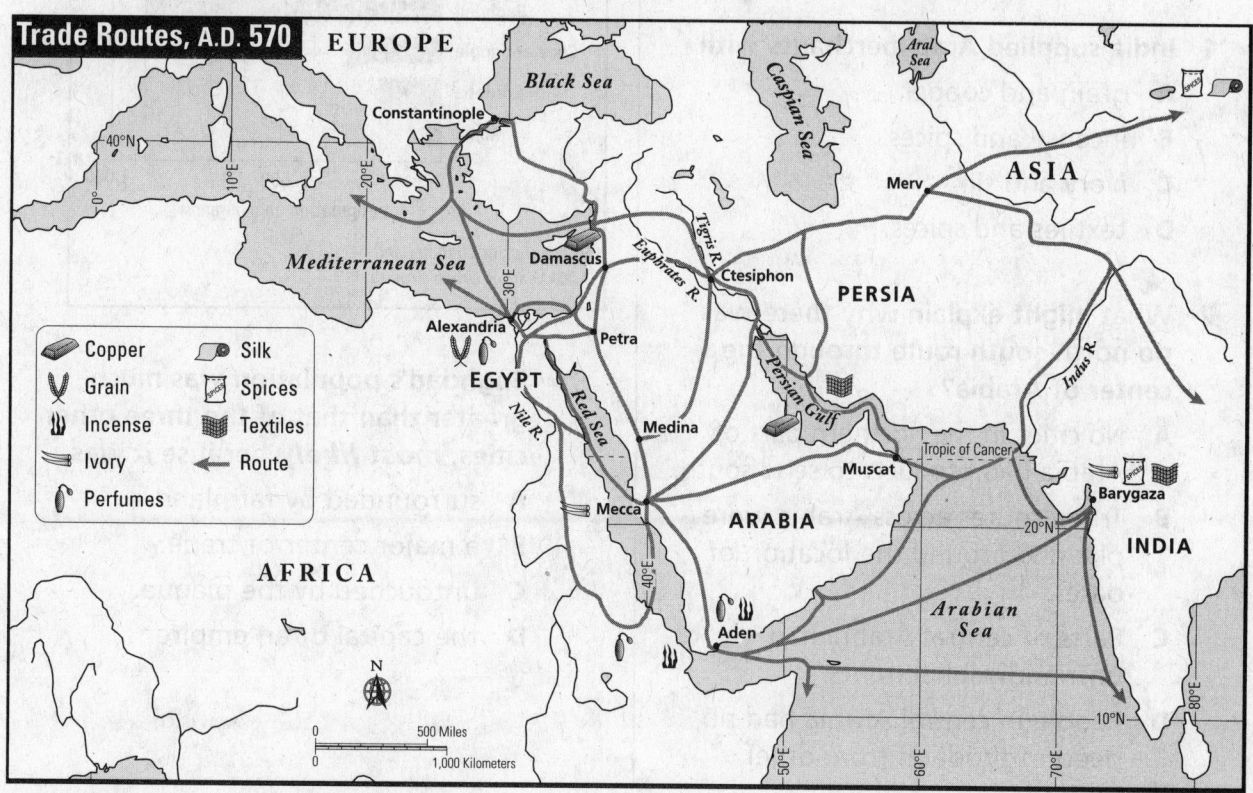

Growth of Trade and Cities

By the 600s, many Arabs lived in market towns. As a result of trade, these market towns grew into cities. In particular, the settlements on the western coast of Arabia became important centers of local, regional, and long-distance trade. Trade routes for camel caravans ran from oasis to oasis from the southern tip of the peninsula to the Byzantine and Persian empires to the north.

Baghdad, established in the late 700s, became a major trading center. Baghdad's merchants traveled as far as China, India, Northern Europe, and Africa. The widespread use of Arabic in the Muslim Empire and the uniform currency helped trade grow.

PRACTICE

CALIFORNIA CONTENT
STANDARD 7.2.5

Trade in the Arab World

DIRECTIONS: Choose the letter of the *best* answer.

Use the map on page 45 to answer questions 1 and 2.

1 India supplied Arab merchants with

   A grain and copper.

   B incense and spices.

   C ivory and silk.

   D textiles and spices.

2 What might explain why there was no north-south route through the center of Arabia?

   A No cities in the northern part of Arabia had products to send south.

   B Trade routes across Arabia were planned around the location of oases.

   C Parts of central Arabia had unfriendly inhabitants.

   D People in central Arabia had no need of products from other regions.

3 Which of the following accurately characterizes trade in the Muslim Empire?

   A Very little internal trade took place.

   B Arab caravans did not extend as far as China.

   C A common currency within the empire made trading easier.

   D Arabia's location was a disadvantage for regional or long-distance trade.

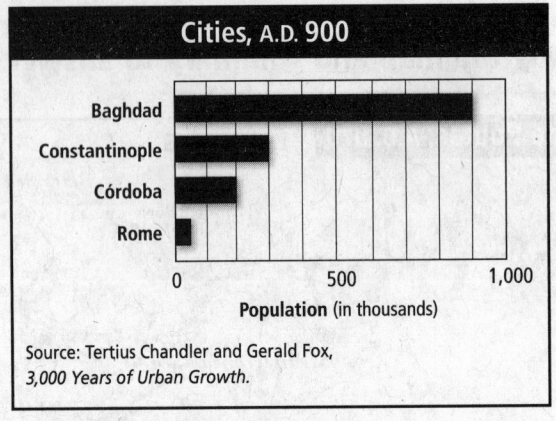

Cities, A.D. 900

Population (in thousands)

Source: Tertius Chandler and Gerald Fox, *3,000 Years of Urban Growth.*

4 Baghdad's population was much greater than that of the three other cities, *most likely* because it was

   A surrounded by farmland.

   B a major center of trade.

   C untouched by the plague.

   D the capital of an empire.

REVIEW

CALIFORNIA CONTENT
STANDARD 7.2.6

The Muslim Legacy

SPECIFIC OBJECTIVE: Understand the intellectual exchanges among Muslim scholars of Eurasia and Africa and the contributions Muslim scholars made to science, geography, mathematics, philosophy, medicine, art, and literature.

Read the chart to answer questions on the next page.

Muslim Contributions to the Arts and Sciences	
Architecture and Art	Muslim art features plant and geometric designs because Muslims believe only God should produce the human form. They used calligraphy, or fine handwriting, to decorate buildings, swords, armor, and books. In architecture, the Muslims adapted features from other cultures, such as the dome and the vault. The Great Mosque of Córdoba, one of the largest houses of worship ever built, used two levels of arches in a way never seen before.
Astronomy	Muslims studied astronomy to determine the exact location of Mecca from other places in the empire and to figure out the correct times for prayer. They made charts that showed the locations of planets at different times of the year and invented instruments to help them observe the skies. They built a planetarium with planets that moved. One mathematician proved that people see objects because rays pass from the objects to the eyes. Later, his work was used to develop lenses for telescopes and microscopes.
Geography	Muslim geographers wrote descriptions of several regions, including Spain, North Africa, and the Arabian Peninsula. One geographer, Al-Idrisi, compiled an encyclopedia of geographic knowledge, containing about 70 maps.
Literature	Muslim literature included works such as *The Thousand and One Nights*. Poetry, particularly the quatrain or 4-line poem, was popular.
Mathematics	Muslim mathematicians based much of their work on ideas from ancient Greeks, Egyptians, and Indians. Al-Khwarizmi borrowed the Indian numeral system, including zero, and developed algebra. Others advanced the study of geometry.
Medicine	Doctors built on theories and ideas from the past. Physicians improved diagnostic methods and added to the understanding of circulation. They wrote medical encyclopedias that were relied upon for many years.
Scholarship	The House of Wisdom in Baghdad contained books on all subjects from many parts of the world. Córdoba had 70 libraries, the largest of which held over 400,000 volumes. In Córdoba, Jewish scholars worked side by side with Muslims to preserve and advance knowledge.
Science	Muslim scientists believed in scientific observation and experimentation to find answers to questions.
Technology	Muslims improved upon papermaking methods of the Chinese. Baghdad became the papermaking center for the empire. This led to greater availability of books.

PRACTICE

CALIFORNIA CONTENT
STANDARD 7.2.6

The Muslim Legacy

Directions: Choose the letter of the *best* answer.

"Acquire knowledge. It enableth its possessor to distinguish right from wrong; it lighteth the way to Heaven. . . ."

—Muhammad,
quoted in *The Sayings of Muhammad*

1 According to the quotation, Muslims should seek knowledge in order to

A help them gain salvation.

B increase their material wealth.

C gain superiority over their friends and family members.

D earn a living.

2 Which Muslim art form adapts features from other cultures?

A woodworking

B calligraphy

C architecture

D decorative arts

3 Why did Muslims begin to study astronomy?

A They wanted to find a more accurate method of navigation.

B They wanted to be able to predict changing seasons accurately.

C They wanted to develop an accurate compass.

D They wanted to determine the location of Mecca and times for prayer.

4 Muslim art often featured geometric designs and images of plants because

A vegetation in the desert was rarely seen.

B geometry was important in Islam.

C Muslims did not draw humans.

D calligraphy is based on geometric design.

5 Muslims' greatest contribution to western civilization was

A using vaults and domes.

B preserving and advancing knowledge from previous cultures.

C discovering that rays pass from objects to the eyes.

D writing an encyclopedia of geography.

REVIEW

CALIFORNIA CONTENT STANDARD 7.3.1

The Tang Dynasty (618–907)

SPECIFIC OBJECTIVE: Describe the reunification of China under the Tang Dynasty and reasons for the spread of Buddhism in Tang China, Korea, and Japan.

Read the summary to answer questions on the next page.

Reunification of China

Several strong Tang rulers completed the work of reunifying China begun in the previous Sui Dynasty.

- Land in the north and west was recovered. Korea was reconquered.
- Civil service examinations were given again. This placed talented candidates in official positions, helping to strengthen the government.
- The road and canal systems were expanded.
- Foreign trade was promoted.
- A land distribution program was begun. Peasants were given land.
- Agricultural methods and farming tools increased food production.
- A law code was written, making laws uniform throughout the empire.

Spread of Buddhism

By the first century, missionaries and merchants from India had brought Buddhist ideas to China. Buddhists believed in the **Four Noble Truths:**

- Life is filled with suffering.
- The cause of this suffering is people's desire for worldly pleasures.
- The way to end all suffering is to end all desires.
- The way to reach enlightenment is to follow the Eightfold Path.

In the chaos and disorder following the collapse of the Han Dynasty in A.D. 220, people were attracted to this message. Buddhism spread rapidly. From China, Buddhism spread to Korea and from there to Japan.

During the Tang Dynasty, Buddhism became a more permanent part of Chinese culture. Different branches developed, including Ch'an or Zen Buddhism. A later Tang emperor suppressed Buddhism to gain the wealth of the Buddhist monasteries. After this, Buddhism in China declined.

Name _____ Date _____

DIRECTIONS: Choose the letter of the *best* answer.

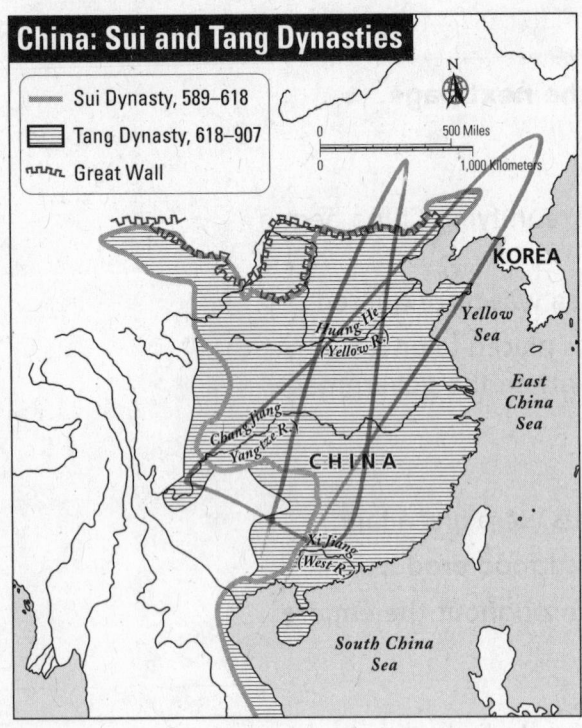

China: Sui and Tang Dynasties

──── Sui Dynasty, 589–618
▦ Tang Dynasty, 618–907
〰〰 Great Wall

0 ___ 500 Miles
0 ___ 1,000 Kilometers

N

KOREA

*Huang He
(Yellow) R.*

*Yellow
Sea*

*East
China
Sea*

*Chang Jiang
(Yangtze) R.*

CHINA

*Xi Jiang
(West) R.*

*South China
Sea*

1 Which observation about the boundaries of China during the Sui and Tang Dynasties is accurate, based on the map?

A Korea was part of China during the Sui Dynasty.

B The greatest gain in land during the Sui period was to the east and south.

C The most substantial expansion during the Tang period was in the west.

D China's Great Wall protected its territory completely by the end of the Tang Dynasty.

2 What was *one* result of giving the civil service examination again during the Tang Dynasty?

A Many government officials lost their jobs.

B Government positions were staffed by generally qualified candidates.

C Taxes increased.

D Corruption among government officials developed in the competition for jobs.

Wu Zhao was the only woman to take the title of emperor. She ruled during the Tang Dynasty. Wu Zhao cut taxes, raised the salaries of government officials, reduced expensive military operations, and reformed the government.

3 What most likely led Wu Zhao to take the steps written in the description above?

A She did not believe in the use of military force.

B She wanted to win the loyalty of the people.

C She wanted to encourage rebellion throughout the empire.

D She had a plan to weaken China.

REVIEW

CALIFORNIA CONTENT STANDARD 7.3.2

Tang and Sung Achievements

SPECIFIC OBJECTIVE: Describe agricultural, technological, and commercial developments during the Tang and Sung periods.

Read the cluster diagram to answer questions on the next page.

Agricultural

- Growth of new rice that yielded two or three harvests a year
- Government distribution of rice seedlings to all farmers
- Increase in farmland through methods such as terracing hillsides and draining marshes with pumps and canals

Commercial

- Expansion of foreign trade via the Silk Roads
- Expansion of sea trade to Korea, Japan, India, Persia, and Africa as a result of improved shipbuilding techniques
- Increase in internal trade as a result of improved roads and canals
- Establishment of trading colonies around Southeast Asia
- Exportation of tea, porcelain, and Buddhism
- Invention of paper money
- Growth of iron industry and mining

Tang and Sung Achievements

Technological

- Development of a magnetic compass
- Ability to manufacture paper in large quantities
- Invention of wood-block printing and movable type
- Printing of first books
- Invention of gunpowder

- Creation of porcelain
- Invention of the mechanical clock
- Use of negative numbers
- Construction of giant ships powered by sails and oars

PRACTICE

CALIFORNIA CONTENT
STANDARD 7.3.2

Tang and Sung Achievements

DIRECTIONS: Choose the letter of the *best* answer.

1 How did the increase in farmland and rice production most likely affect ancient China?

A An increased food supply led to a growth in population.

B A decreased need for farmers led to high unemployment.

C Greater farming success made the Chinese rebel against their government.

D China became more desirable to invaders.

2 What advantage did paper money offer merchants over coins or precious metals?

A Paper money was easier to carry and use in large amounts.

B Paper money was universally accepted.

C Paper money had more value than coins or precious metals.

D Paper money could be printed by the merchants themselves whenever they needed it.

3 As a result of the vigorous trade during the Tang and Sung dynasties,

A China's supply of natural resources decreased.

B China imported more than it exported.

C China's culture spread to many areas.

D China remained isolated from other cultures.

4 The growth of the bureaucracy during the Tang and Sung dynasties is directly related to

A the use of negative numbers.

B the development of the compass.

C an increased need for paper.

D the growth of the iron industry.

5 What made the exchange of technological and scientific ideas easier during the Tang and Sung (Song) period?

A internal unrest

B growth of cities

C high unemployment

D government restrictions

6 Based on the achievements of the Tang and Sung dynasties, which inference might be made?

A The Tang and Sung dynasties were generally a time of stability and prosperity in China.

B Many foreign wars were fought during the Tang and Sung dynasties, leading to the need for more advanced weaponry.

C Under Tang and Sung rulers, individuality and creativity were stifled.

D Tang and Sung achievements were a response to problems such as hunger and disease.

REVIEW

**CALIFORNIA CONTENT
STANDARD 7.3.3**

Confucianism

SPECIFIC OBJECTIVE: Analyze the influences of Confucianism and changes in Confucian thought during the Sung and Mongol periods.

Read the summary and chart to answer questions on the next page.

Confucianism lost favor after the fall of the Han Dynasty in 220. It became popular again in the seventh century. Its focus was shifted due to the influence of Buddhism. Education was still important, but it was seen as a way to achieve morality, not simply a means of advancing in life.

In keeping with the Confucian belief that government was built on the skill of its people, the Sui Dynasty started to give the civil service examination once more. Those who passed the test received government positions. This method of awarding government jobs meant that the most qualified and capable Chinese men were in charge of the country's affairs.

618–907	Tang emperors built upon Confucian ideas of government. They expanded the civil service exam. The result was a complex and advanced government system, staffed by an elite group of scholar-officials.
960–1279	Under the Sung (Song) Dynasty, the civil service exam was improved and included more practical subjects. This expanded the number of scholar-officials and drew them from classes other than the wealthy upper class. More schools were started to increase the number of educated candidates.
1279–1368	The Mongols kept the organization of the Chinese government, but they discontinued the state exam. They kept the Chinese out of high government offices and instead appointed Mongols or foreigners to these posts. The Chinese served as local officials. Under Kublai Khan, Confucianism won back some acceptance. Later the state examinations were started again, but good results on the test did not guarantee a government position.

Name _____   Date _____

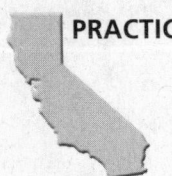
𝒞onfucianism

4/5

DIRECTIONS: Choose the letter of the *best* answer.

1 What changed the focus of
Confucianism to the morality of the
individual through education?

A the Mongol invasion

B the exposure to Buddhism

C the opening of the Silk Roads

D the end of the Tang Dynasty

2 Which dynasty can be given credit
for reestablishing the civil service
examination as a way to select
government officials?

A Sung Dynasty

B Sui Dynasty

C Tang Dynasty

D Yuan Dynasty (Mongols)

3 What was the Confucian reasoning
behind the use of an exam
to determine who would win
government positions?

A A spirit of competition led to
better candidates.

B People who did not study for the
exam would not work hard in a
job.

C China would flourish only if the
upper class kept the upper hand.

D Good government could result
only if skilled people were in
charge.

4 Why were more schools established
during the Sung Dynasty?

A to produce more eligible
candidates for government

B to train youths to become soldiers

C to reverse the Tang Dynasty trend
of minimizing education

D to prepare Chinese merchants for
foreign trade

He adopted the Chinese system of
government, had his children given
a Chinese education. However, he
imposed a four-level structure on
society that put the Mongols on the
top and the Chinese at the bottom.

—about Kublai Khan

---

5 What can be inferred about the
Mongols and Confucianism from this
passage?

A Mongols kept all Confucian
standards.

B Confucian standards no longer
determined government positions.

C The Mongols had their own type
of civil service exam.

D Mongols studied Confucianism to
win government positions.

REVIEW

CALIFORNIA CONTENT
STANDARD 7.3.4

China Trade in the Yuan and Ming Dynasties

SPECIFIC OBJECTIVE: Understand the importance of both overland trade and maritime expeditions between China and other civilizations in the Mongol Ascendancy and Ming Dynasty.

Read the summary to answer questions on the next page.

Trade under the Mongols

Mongol control of Eurasia created stability, security, and peace. This time was known as *Pax Mongolica.* Traders and travelers were guaranteed safety as they traveled the Silk Roads or roads in any part of the empire. As a result, trade between China and the West increased. Merchants carried inventions, such as gunpowder, printing technology, the compass, and paper money to the West, in addition to products such as silk and porcelain.

Chinese merchants brought new foods, plants, and minerals back from their trips. Many merchants, missionaries, and other travelers from India, Central Asia, Persia, and Europe visited China and learned about its culture.

Trade and Travel during the Ming Dynasty (1368–1644)

Under Yonglo, who began his rule in 1403, seven major sea voyages were launched. These voyages, led by Zheng He, had two purposes. One goal was to explore new regions. The other was to impress foreign regions with China's power so that they would pay tribute. Zheng He set sail with between 40 and 300 huge ships in each expedition. During each voyage, he distributed gifts of silver and silk to show Chinese superiority.

As a result of Zheng He's voyages, trade increased and China's reputation grew. Several countries did sent tribute. Nevertheless, scholar-officials complained that the voyages wasted valuable resources and China withdrew into isolation.

To enforce the isolation policy, only the government was allowed to trade with foreigners. Still, demand for Chinese goods increased. Unofficially, Chinese merchants smuggled cargoes of silk, porcelain, and other valuable goods to European buyers. Industries, including silk making and ceramics, grew rapidly.

Despite increased manufacturing activity, China remained a mainly agricultural country. The government continued to favor farming. Confucian beliefs looked down upon commerce.

Name _____ Date _____

PRACTICE

CALIFORNIA CONTENT STANDARD 7.3.4

China Trade in the Yuan and Ming Dynasties

DIRECTIONS: Choose the letter of the *best* answer.

Use the map to answer questions 1 and 2.

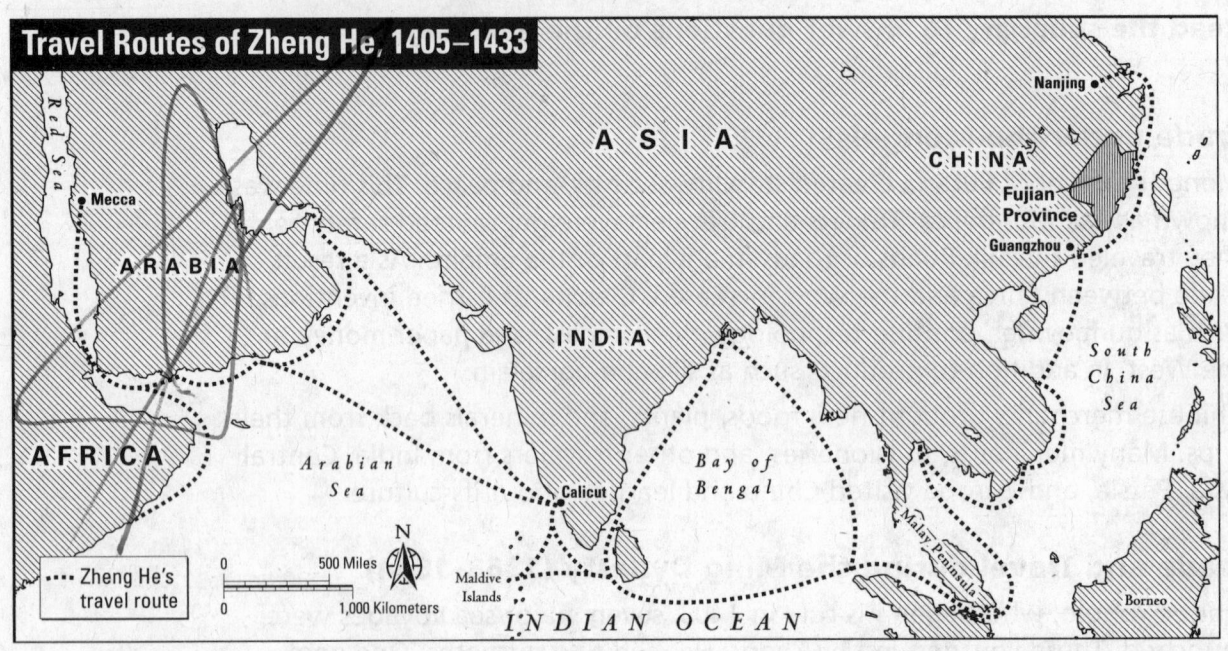

Travel Routes of Zheng He, 1405–1433

- - - Zheng He's travel route

0   500 Miles
0   1,000 Kilometers

Red Sea · Mecca · ARABIA · AFRICA · Arabian Sea · Calicut · Maldive Islands · INDIAN OCEAN · ASIA · INDIA · Bay of Bengal · Malay Peninsula · Borneo · CHINA · Nanjing · Fujian Province · Guangzhou · South China Sea

1 **According to the map, what conclusion can be drawn about China in the time of Zheng He?**

A China's advanced technology let sailors undertake long voyages.

B The Chinese rarely went far from their own region.

C For the Chinese sailors, navigation was still a mystery.

D Chinese sailors needed to stay within sight of the coast.

2 **Why was Zheng He sent on the voyages shown on the map?**

A to set up colonies that would ease the overcrowding in China

B to discover a faster route to Europe

C to explore new lands and gain more tribute-paying states

D to identify potentially hostile regions

56 CSS Specific Objective 7.3.4: Practice

REVIEW

CALIFORNIA CONTENT STANDARD 7.3.5   *Effect of China's Inventions*

SPECIFIC OBJECTIVE: Trace the historic influence of such discoveries as tea, the manufacture of paper, wood-block printing, the compass, and gunpowder.

Read the chart to answer questions on the next page.

Importance of Chinese Inventions		
	Description	**Impact**
Tea (2700 B.C.)	Beverage produced from tea leaves soaked in hot water	Chinese used tea as medicine first, then it became a popular drink; exported to Europe
Methods of making paper (A.D. 105)	Made from fibers, rags, fishnets, and hemp waste	Ability to produce paper in quantity allowed Chinese to record their knowledge permanently; spread to Europe in the 1100s
Porcelain (late A.D. 700s)	Bone-hard, white ceramic made of a special clay and a mineral found only in China	Became a valuable export—so associated with Chinese culture that it is now called china; technology remained a Chinese secret for centuries
Mechanical clock (A.D. 700s)	Clock in which machinery (driven by running water) regulated the movements	Early Chinese clocks short-lived; idea for mechanical clock carried by traders to medieval Europe
Printing Block printing (A.D. 700s) Movable type (A.D. 1040)	Block printing: one block on which a whole page is cut; movable type: individual characters arranged in frames, used over and over	Printing technology spread to Korea and Japan; movable type also developed later in Europe
Explosive powder (A.D. 800s)	Made from mixture of saltpeter, sulfur, and charcoal	First used for fireworks, then weapons; technology spread west within 300 years and brought about the invention of deadly new weapons, which helped to end feudalism in Europe
Paper money (A.D. 1020s)	Paper currency issued by Sung government to replace cumbersome strings of metal cash used by merchants	Contributed to development of large-scale commercial economy in China
Magnetic compass (for navigation) (A.D. 1100s)	Floating magnetized needle that always points north-south; device had existed in China for centuries before it was adapted by sailors for use at sea	Helped China become a sea power; technology quickly spread west and helped make the European Age of Exploration possible.

PRACTICE

CALIFORNIA CONTENT STANDARD 7.3.5

Effect of China's Inventions

DIRECTIONS: Choose the letter of the *best* answer.

1 Why is porcelain often called china?

A China was the only manufacturer of porcelain for centuries.

B Its main ingredient is a clay called china.

C China refers to how delicate and fragile it is.

D China is the Chinese name for porcelain.

2 Why was the development of explosive powder historically important?

A It was the reason that the Mongols were able to invade China.

B Its use changed the nature of warfare.

C Chinese exportation of the powder became a major business.

D It is used in fireworks.

3 Which invention had a regional rather than a global impact?

A paper money

B porcelain

C printing trade

D tea

4 Which event or trend could be considered the result of the magnetic compass?

A the fall of the feudal system

B the construction of larger and more powerful ships

C the discovery of America

D the conquest of Korea by China

5 Which of the following 20th century inventions might be considered comparable in its effect to the development of printing technology?

A antibiotics

B the Internet

C space shuttle

D atomic bomb

6 What conclusion might be drawn based on the chart?

A During the Tang and Sung dynasties, Chinese ingenuity reached a peak.

B Most of the products first invented by the Chinese were later invented independently by the Europeans.

C Under the isolationist policy of Ming China, most Chinese technologies were kept secret.

D Chinese innovations were mostly concerned with increasing food production.

Name _____

SPECIFIC OBJECTIVE: Describe the development of the imperial state and the scholar-official class.

Read the diagram and summary to answer questions on the next page.

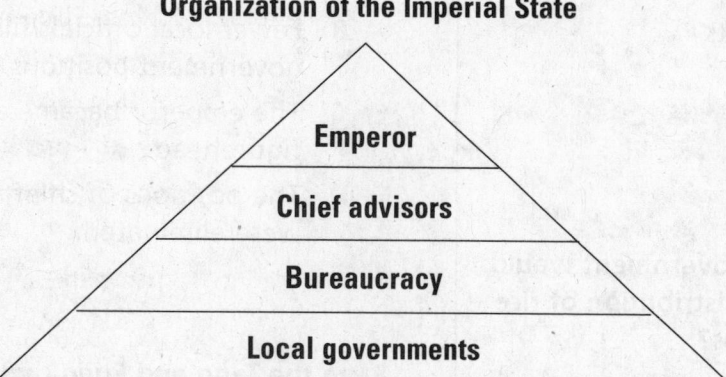

Organization of the Imperial State

- Emperor
- Chief advisors
- Bureaucracy
- Local governments

The Tang Dynasty

Under the Tang Dynasty, the government became more efficient. Chief advisors served the emperor directly. The bureaucracy had many different departments. These departments were in charge of the empire's affairs, including taxes, agriculture, and the military. Local governments reported to the bureaucracy.

The civil service examination became a means to select capable career bureaucrats. Those who passed were known as scholar-officials. During the Tang Dynasty, these were mostly from wealthy families, who could afford the education necessary to pass the civil service test. Some scholar-officials received their positions through political favors. In time, doing well on the test became more important than having a noble background. As a result, more candidates began to earn their positions because of their talent and education.

The Sung Dynasty

The Sung (Song) Dynasty centralized power even further by replacing regional officials, such as governors, with scholar-officials more closely connected to the palace. The opening of more schools also helped men who were not wealthy or of noble birth to become scholar-officials.

The power of the aristocracy declined during the Tang and Sung dynasties. A new upper class, composed of scholar-officials and their families, developed. The members of this class were known as the gentry.

e Chinese Imperial State

DIRECTIONS: Choose the letter of the *best* answer.

1 Who had the *least* power in the imperial state?

A the chief advisors

B local governments

C the emperor

D the bureaucracy

2 Which part of the government would be responsible for distribution of rice or collection of taxes?

A advisors

B bureaucracy

C emperor

D local government

3 What was *one* advantage of having civil servants rather than appointing nobles to fill government positions?

A There were not enough nobles to fill the positions.

B Nobles demanded too much pay.

C Nobles were unfriendly to the emperor.

D Not all nobles were skilled or capable.

4 What change was brought about during the Sung Dynasty?

A The bureaucracy was reduced.

B Fewer local officials filled government positions.

C The emperor became a figurehead.

D The positions of chief advisors were eliminated.

5 In the Tang and Sung dynasties, the new gentry gained social status through

A noble birth.

B employment.

C land ownership.

D trade and commerce.

6 What fact suggests that the state examination was very challenging?

A The Mongols discontinued the use of the state exam to select officials.

B Chinese writing has about 40,000 symbols.

C Fewer than 30 scholars passed the test each year.

D Scholar-officials were very well educated.

**CALIFORNIA CONTENT
STANDARD 7.4.1**

Ghana and Mali

SPECIFIC OBJECTIVE: Study the Niger River and the relationship of vegetation zones to trade and the growth of the Ghana and Mali empires.

Study the map and read the text to answer questions on the next page.

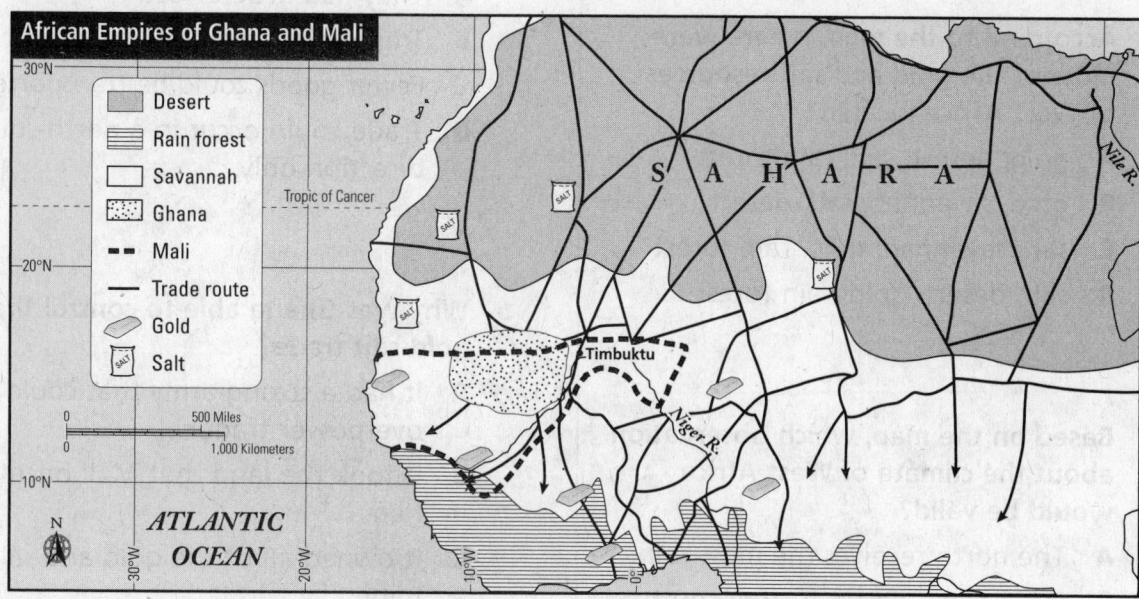

Trans-Saharan Trade

- Salt was mined in the Sahara Desert and traded for gold from the south, as well as crops and enslaved laborers from the flat, grassy plains of the savannah region.

- Around the fourth century, camels began to be used in trade caravans. They could travel long distances without water, making the journeys easier.

Ghana (800–1076)

- Ghana was located where salt from the north met the gold and enslaved Africans from the south. Ghana controlled the gold-salt trade.

- Ghana's king taxed trade and demanded tribute, or payment, from nearby tribes.

- Ghana conquered more territories. Large trading cities sprang up, and the kingdom grew wealthy.

Mali (1235–1400s)

- New sources of gold were found farther east. As a result, the trade routes moved closer to Mali.

- Under the ruler Sundiata, Mali took control of the gold-salt trade. Mali grew wealthy and powerful. It expanded to include Ghana's former territory.

- Mali's city of Timbuktu, at the crossroads of the desert and savannah, became a center for trade and learning.

PRACTICE

CALIFORNIA CONTENT
STANDARD 7.4.1

Ghana and Mali

DIRECTIONS: Choose the letter of the *best* answer.

Use the map on page 61 to answer questions 1 and 2.

1 According to the map, where were most of the gold and salt resources of West Africa located?

   A gold, desert; salt, rain forest

   B gold, savannah; salt, desert

   C salt, savannah; gold, rain forest

   D salt, desert; gold, rain forest

2 Based on the map, which observation about the climate of West Africa would be valid?

   A The north receives the most rain.

   B It becomes wetter further south.

   C The center is the most rainy area.

   D All areas get equal rainfall.

3 In Ghana, crops grew best in

   A the savannah

   B the rain forests

   C the Sahara

   D Timbuktu

4 How did the use of camels most likely affect trade?

   A They had little effect.

   B Trans-Saharan trade increased.

   C Fewer goods could be transported.

   D Trade could occur in a north-south direction only.

5 Why was Ghana able to control the gold-salt trade?

   A It had a strong army that could overpower traders.

   B It took the land that Mali once had.

   C It owned all of the gold and salt mines.

   D It was located at the meeting point for gold and salt traders.

6 What was one result of the shift in trade routes?

   A Ghana grew stronger.

   B Gold's value declined.

   C Trans-Saharan trade decreased.

   D Mali gained control of the gold-salt trade.

REVIEW

CALIFORNIA CONTENT STANDARD 7.4.2

Early West African Society

SPECIFIC OBJECTIVE: Analyze the importance of family, labor specialization, and regional commerce in West Africa.

Read the summary to answer questions on the next page.

Family Life

The kinship group was the basic social unit of West African society. Kinship refers to a connection among people based on blood, marriage, or adoption. Within West African society, kinship groups were governed by a council of elders, which had representatives from each group. Kinship groups with a common ancestor formed clans. Although kings or emperors might have controlled the region, ordinary West Africans had little contact with them.

Work Roles

Farming was a major occupation for many West Africans. Each member of the family had a function to perform. For example, women made the food and worked in the fields. Men looked after the large animals and built the houses and fences. Children did other tasks, such as taking care of the flocks.

Labor specialization enabled West Africa to become a diverse economy. People did specific types of work, such as farming, herding, or trading. West Africans were skilled traders. They were also skilled iron workers. Their iron tools and weapons helped make their communities richer. This in turn attracted more people to move to their villages and cities.

Regional Commerce

By the fourth century, trade between West Africa and North Africa was expanding. In exchange for salt, cloth, and metal from North Africa, West Africans traded gold, enslaved people, ivory, and cattle hides. Cities developed from the early trading centers. These cities also became centers of education, politics, and religion.

Kings eventually gained power and took control of these trade systems. The kings kept their power in part because their policies benefited the people. The kings also served a religious function for the society. People believed the king's prayers and rituals could bring rain or prosperity to the region.

PRACTICE

CALIFORNIA CONTENT STANDARD 7.4.2

Early West African Society

DIRECTIONS: Choose the letter of the *best* answer.

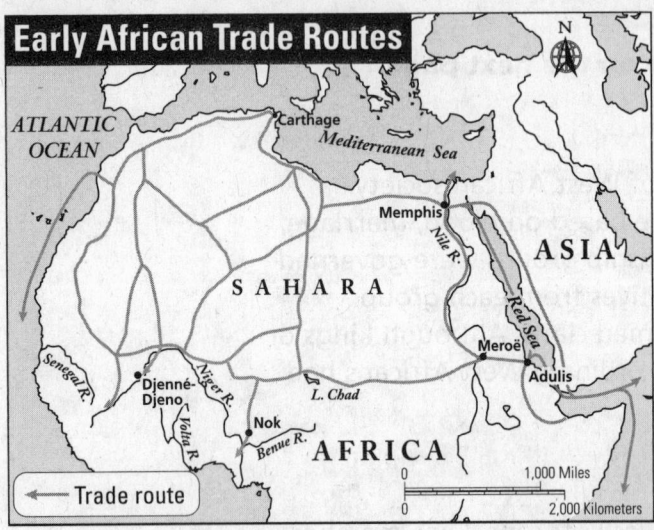

Early African Trade Routes

ATLANTIC OCEAN

Carthage

Mediterranean Sea

Memphis

Nile R.

ASIA

SAHARA

Red Sea

Meroë

Adulis

Senegal R.

Djenné-Djeno

Niger R.

Volta R.

L. Chad

Nok

Benue R.

AFRICA

0   1,000 Miles

0   2,000 Kilometers

⟵ Trade route

1 According to the map, how did most early traders in Africa move their goods?

A by overland caravans

B by ship via sea routes

C by boats on the rivers

D first by sea and then by land

2 To whom did the West Africans feel the greatest loyalty?

A members of their clan

B the village elders

C their kinship group

D their king

3 Labor specialization occurs when people

A farm the same crop.

B develop skills in different jobs.

C share the tasks of the household.

D contribute to the economy of the village or town.

4 Which factors helped West African societies to become wealthy?

A family farms and iron technology

B iron technology and trade

C labor specialization and rule by elders

D strength of family bonds and trade

5 How did increasingly complex trade systems lead to the development of kingdoms?

A Traders wanted to do business only with people in authority.

B Government was needed to impose order along trade routes.

C Religious leaders founded dynasties in trading areas.

D Strong individuals gained support to take control of trade systems.

REVIEW

CALIFORNIA CONTENT STANDARD 7.4.3

Influence of Trans-Saharan Trade on West Africa

SPECIFIC OBJECTIVE: Describe the role of the trans-Saharan caravan trade in the changing religious and cultural characteristics of West Africa and the influence of Islamic beliefs, ethics, and law.

Read the chart to answer questions on the next page.

Impact of Trans-Saharan Trade

Berber nomads from North Africa established trade routes with West Africans. In addition to the goods they traded, they also spread Islamic ideas that influenced aspects of West African societies.

Religion
- Some rulers and members of the upper classes converted to Islam. Several rulers practiced their traditional religion as well. This helped them keep their authority over their people.
- In the empire of Mali, devout Muslim rulers helped spread Islam further. Mansa Musa, ruler of Mali from 1312 to 1322, made an elaborate hajj, or pilgrimage to Mecca.
- The majority of common people followed their traditional animistic beliefs. Animism is a belief in spirits living in animals, plants, and natural forces.
- Over the centuries, more West Africans adapted Islamic practices. They developed their own type of Islam.

Culture
- Islam influenced styles of architecture in West Africa. Muslim rulers oversaw the construction of many mosques in this part of Africa. These mosques often combined Islamic and West African features. For example, they had minarets, or tall towers, but they were built of mud brick.
- Berbers introduced new weaving techniques and the horizontal loom.
- Islamic geometric design expanded the West Africans' use of these patterns.
- Other aspects of Muslim culture were adapted to local customs or, as in the case of women veiling their faces, were ignored completely in West African Muslim communities.

Ethics and Law
- Islamic ideas about law and right and wrong influenced West African societies. This was a result of the large number of Muslims who had positions of authority in the government.
- In many cases, a compromise between Muslim and traditional law or ethics was established. In other cases, local tradition was followed.
- Later West African rulers included more Islamic features in their governments. The Songhai emperor Askia Muhammad appointed Muslim judges, bringing the legal system further in line with Islamic principles. He created a large bureaucracy staffed by Arab Muslims.

Name _____ Date _____

PRACTICE

CALIFORNIA CONTENT
STANDARD 7.4.3

Influence of Trans-Saharan Trade on West Africa

DIRECTIONS: Choose the letter of the *best* answer.

1 Why were the Berbers significant in the history of West Africa?

A They built great cities.

B They established trade routes and spread Islam.

C They mined the gold that was traded for salt.

D They conquered Ghana and Mali.

2 How might the influence of Islam upon the religious practices of West Africa be summarized?

A Islam was adopted eagerly by all.

B Some adopted Islam, while others kept traditional beliefs.

C With time, fewer West Africans practiced Islam.

D More West Africans believed in animism once Islam was introduced.

3 What did Muslim and West African artists have in common?

A They portrayed the human form realistically.

B They decorated everything with calligraphy.

C They used geometric designs in their art.

D They both depicted their gods in sculptures.

When Ibn Battuta arrived there, the casual interaction between men and women shocked him. Ibn Battuta expressed his disapproval and then promptly left the house.

4 In the passage, what is revealed by the scene Ibn Battuta witnesses and by his reaction?

A West Africans followed the Muslim practice of keeping women and men separate.

B West African Muslims did not follow all Islamic customs.

C Ibn Battuta enjoyed the freedom of society in Mali.

D There were no devout Muslims in Mali.

5 How did government in West Africa change after the introduction of Islam?

A The influence of the Qur'an on West African laws increased.

B There was no change in West African government.

C The emperor was replaced by a caliph who built a Muslim empire.

D The government lost control of the gold-salt trade.

Copyright © McDougal Littell/Houghton Mifflin Company

66 CSS Specific Objective 7.4.3: Practice

REVIEW

CALIFORNIA CONTENT STANDARD 7.4.4

Growth of the Arabic Language in West Africa

SPECIFIC OBJECTIVE: Trace the growth of the Arabic language in government, trade, and Islamic scholarship in West Africa.

Read the summary to answer questions on the next page.

Growth of Arabic

Some kingdoms in Africa, such as Egypt and Nubia, had writing systems. However, it was not until Islam was introduced into West Africa that literacy and knowledge of writing started to spread. Converts to Islam had to know Arabic in order to study the Qur'an. In addition, Muslims, who used written language, gained positions of authority in West African governments. Arabic then became the language of government.

Literacy led to greater emphasis on education. Trading centers became centers of scholarship. The most famous of these cities is Timbuktu.

Timbuktu

Under the Mali ruler Mansa Musa, Timbuktu grew into a center of Islamic learning and culture. Mansa Musa brought back scholars and artisans from his pilgrimage to Mecca. He had huge libraries and universities built. As a result, Timbuktu attracted poets, scholars, and artists from all over Africa and the Middle East. Even though the empire of Mali fell, Timbuktu remained a stronghold of Islamic culture. It became even more famous during the reign of Askia Muhammad, a ruler of the Songhai empire. He relied on the scholars for legal advice. During his rule, the University of Sankore had over 25,000 students.

PRACTICE

CALIFORNIA CONTENT
STANDARD 7.4.4

Growth of the Arabic Language in West Africa

DIRECTIONS: Choose the letter of the *best* answer.

1 **Which statement about language in Africa is accurate?**

A West Africa was the only area without a written language.

B Some regions had written language; others did not.

C All groups in Africa had a writing system and large libraries.

D Africans depended on Egyptian hieroglyphics to record their ideas.

2 **Why did many West Africans learn Arabic?**

A to communicate with each other

B to write to other kingdoms

C to study the Qur'an

D to keep village records

3 **Why were many Muslims able to obtain positions in government?**

A They knew how to read and write.

B They were friends of the king.

C They controlled the trade.

D They had previous government experience.

4 **What resulted from the introduction of Arabic to West Africa?**

A more trade

B stronger governments

C greater literacy

D the oral tradition

5 **The development of Timbuktu into a center of culture was the result of**

A an interest in learning inspired by the spread of Arabic.

B Mansa Musa's desire to rival Rome.

C a need to find jobs for scholars and artisans brought from Mecca.

D an increase in trade in the Mali empire.

_____

". . . in Timbuktu. . . . Many hand-written books . . . are also sold. There is more profit made from this commerce than from all other merchandise."

—Leo Africanus from *The Description of Africa* trans. by Paul Brians

6 **Based on the passage above, a major business in Timbuktu was**

A printing books.

B selling books.

C selling any kind of merchandise.

D working for the king.

REVIEW

CALIFORNIA CONTENT STANDARD 7.4.5

Africa's Written and Oral Traditions

SPECIFIC OBJECTIVE: Describe the importance of written and oral traditions in the transmission of African history and culture.

Read the summary to answer questions on the next page.

Most early African societies did not have a written language. Before the introduction of Arabic to West Africa, Arab travelers wrote some information down about these groups. Mostly, the Africans preserved their culture and history through a strong oral tradition.

The West African Oral Tradition

Storytellers, known as griots, told tales about people and the spirits of the natural world. These stories were often sung accompanied by music. The stories had many purposes. They entertained. They passed on the cultural values of the group to the younger generation. They also retold the history of the clan or kinship group so that it would be remembered.

Griots often took part in religious rituals. In these ceremonies, they were seen as intermediaries between the dead ancestors and the people. West Africans believed that their ancestors watched over them. They turned to their ancestors for protection and for favors.

Griots performed for kings and for the villagers. They often acted out parts of their stories. The audience often took part as well. Griots are still an important part of the West African oral tradition.

"I am a griot . . .master in the art of eloquence [skillful talking] . . . We are vessels of speech, we are the repositories [storehouses] which harbor secrets many centuries old . . . Without us the names of kings would vanish . . . We are the memory of mankind; by the spoken word we bring to life the deeds . . . of kings for younger generations . . . For the world is old, but the future springs from the past."

—Djeli Mamoudou Kouyate, from *Sundiata, an Epic of Old Mali*

PRACTICE

CALIFORNIA CONTENT
STANDARD 7.4.5

Africa's Written and
Oral Traditions

DIRECTIONS: Choose the letter of the *best* answer.

1 What function did stories serve in the West African oral tradition?

   A They filled listeners in on current events.

   B Clans used stories to communicate news to each other.

   C They entertained while preserving history and traditions.

   D Stories passed on the language to the young people of the clan.

2 Which of the following is comparable to the role of the griot in West African society?

   A scientist

   B military leader

   C lawyer

   D historian

3 According to the quotation on page 69, griots were significant in West African society because

   A the past they remembered was the key to the future.

   B they knew many secrets that could not be written down.

   C few West Africans were skilled enough to be griots.

   D they had known many kings who were now dead.

4 In what way might written and oral versions of the same story be different?

   A The written version would be longer and include more detail.

   B The oral version would change slightly each time it was told.

   C The written version would have a different ending.

   D The oral version would be more difficult to understand.

REVIEW

CALIFORNIA CONTENT STANDARD 7.5.1

Influence of Korea and China on Japan

SPECIFIC OBJECTIVE: Describe the significance of Japan's proximity to China and Korea and the intellectual, linguistic, religious, and philosophical influence of those countries on Japan.

Read the chart to answer questions on the next page.

Korean travelers and missionaries first brought ideas from the Chinese civilization to Japan. Later, groups of Japanese went to China to study its culture for themselves. The Japanese adapted features from China to make them part of their own culture.

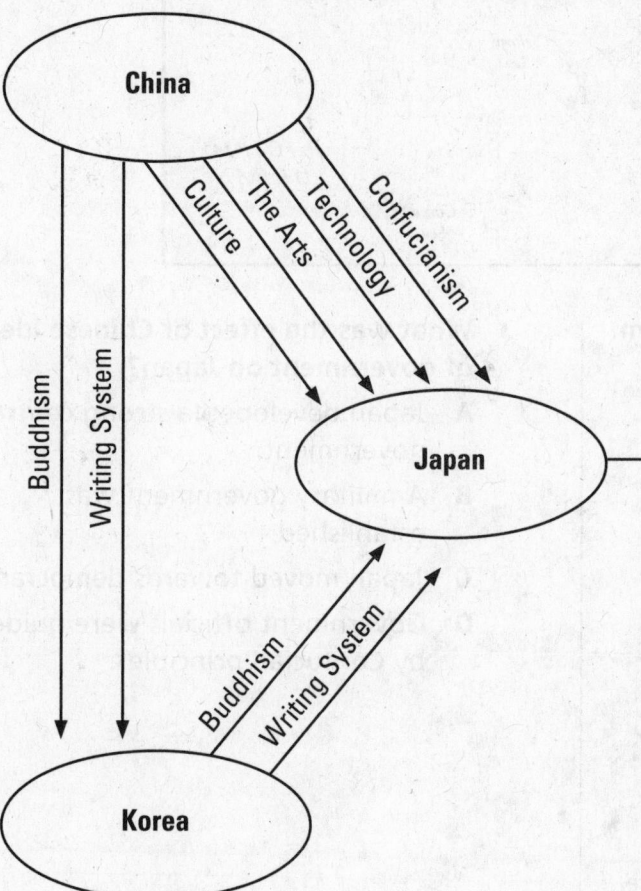

Religion
The Japanese combined Buddhism with their Shinto religion. Shinto was based on respect for the forces of nature and ancestor worship. Buddhist rituals became part of Shinto.

Government
Japanese rulers such as Prince Shotoku worked on building a strong central government similar to the Chinese government.

Culture
The Japanese adopted Chinese styles of cooking, gardening, drinking tea, and even hairdressing. They based their system of writing on Chinese characters.

The Arts
Japanese artists borrowed techniques and themes from the Chinese painters. In addition, Japanese architecture incorporated features of China's.

Agriculture
Japan began to raise rice using the wet-field method of the Chinese.

PRACTICE

CALIFORNIA CONTENT STANDARD 7.5.1

Influence of Korea and China on Japan

DIRECTIONS: Choose the letter of the *best* answer.

Use the map to answer questions 1 and 2.

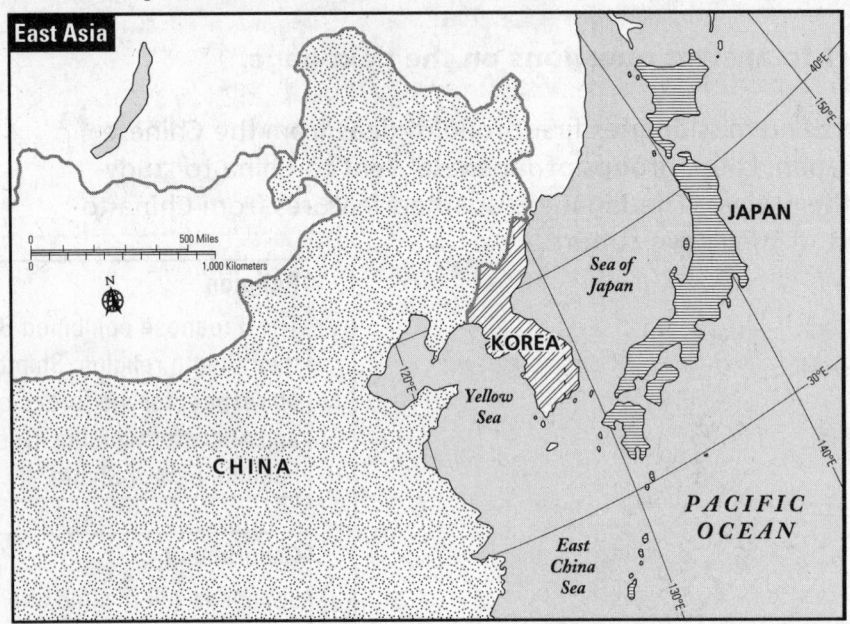

East Asia

1 Approximately how far is Japan from Korea at its closest point?

A 75 miles

B 120 miles

C 250 miles

D 500 miles

2 Based on the map, which statement about Japan's location is valid?

A Its location allowed China to invade easily.

B It occupies a central position in East Asia.

C Its closeness to China enabled the spread of Chinese ideas into Japan.

D Its location was convenient for Chinese to visit on their way to Korea.

3 What was the effect of Chinese ideas of government on Japan?

A Japan developed a strong central government.

B A military government was established.

C Japan moved towards democracy.

D Government officials were guided by Confucian principles.

Name _____   Date _____

REVIEW

CALIFORNIA CONTENT
STANDARD 7.5.2

The Reign of Prince Shotoku (593–622)

SPECIFIC OBJECTIVE: Discuss the reign of Prince Shotoku of Japan and the characteristics of Japanese society and family life during his reign.

Read the list to answer questions on the next page.

Early Japan was made up of many clans. They fought frequently over land. Society was basically organized into nobles, common workers, and some enslaved people. By the fifth century, the Yamato clan had established itself as the most powerful. Prince Shotoku, a member of this clan, ruled Japan for his aunt from 593–622. During his reign, he brought about many changes in Japanese culture and government.

Prince Shotoku's Accomplishments

- Opened relations with China as an equal, not a tribute-paying state
- Brought Chinese scholars, artists, and craftsmen to Japan
- Adopted the Chinese calendar
- Built many highways
- Undertook irrigation projects
- Carried out social welfare reforms
- Constructed major Buddhist temples
- Promoted Buddhism and Confucianism
- Adapted policies designed to strengthen the central government and incorporate Confucian ideals
- Organized the court through a ranking system with each level named for different Confucian values, such as virtue, humanity, faith, knowledge. Officials wore different color caps to distinguish their rank.
- Developed the Seventeen Article Constitution, which established rules for conduct and set forth the ideals of the state. The constitution identified the duties of the ruler, government ministers, and the people. It emphasized the idea of a centralized government and single ruler. It described a bureaucracy based on justice and hard work. It stressed the importance of following Buddhist ideals.

Name _____   Date _____

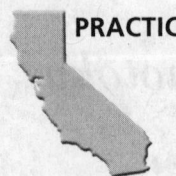 **PRACTICE**

CALIFORNIA CONTENT
STANDARD 7.5.2

The Reign of Prince Shotoku (593–622)

DIRECTIONS: Choose the letter of the *best* answer.

1 Which phrase describes the political organization of early Japan?

  A provinces ruled by governors

  B imperial state supported by a strong bureaucracy

  C military dictatorship

  D individual family groups vying for power

2 By establishing equal relations with China, Prince Shotoku was

  A emphasizing the independence of Japan.

  B trying to frighten China.

  C placing Japan in a position to receive favors.

  D challenging China's position.

3 Prince Shotoku's actions during his reign reveal that he

  A cared little for the common people of Japan.

  B admired China's culture.

  C wanted to reestablish Shinto as the primary religion.

  D had little time for projects other than those related to government.

4 What did Prince Shotoku hope to achieve through his reforms?

  A He wanted to distribute power among the clans.

  B He wanted to make the structure of the government less rigid.

  C He wanted a more centralized and merit-based government.

  D He wanted to return government to the way it had been formerly.

5 Prince Shotoku's emphasis on Confucian ideals in government would suggest that he might have

  A supported family relationships.

  B been willing to employ dishonest means to keep power.

  C felt government officials should inherit, not earn, their positions.

  D believed virtue had an important place in government.

6 Why was the development of the Seventeen Article Constitution historically important?

  A It helped to spread Buddhism.

  B It explained the relationship between Japan and China.

  C It provided guidelines for government and a set of laws for the country.

  D It established guidelines for trade with foreign nations.

CALIFORNIA CONTENT STANDARD 7.5.3

The Lord-Vassal System in Japan

SPECIFIC OBJECTIVE: Describe the values, social customs, and traditions prescribed by the lord-vassal system consisting of *shogun, daimyo,* and *samurai* and the lasting influence of the warrior code in the twentieth century.

Read the summary to answer questions on the next page.

Daimyo and Samurai

Around the eleventh century, the power of the ruling Fujiwara family declined. The government could not control large landholders, known as daimyo. Daimyo began to set up their own armies of samurai. The samurai were warriors who received pay in return for military service. To gain protection, small landowners pledged their loyalty and military service to the daimyo. As a result, the daimyo gained control of large areas of land.

Shogun

By 1192, Minamoto Yoritomo had grown more powerful than the other daimyo. He became shogun, or military dictator of Japan. He ruled for the figurehead emperor. This marked the beginning of the military government.

Bushido

Samurai lived by a code that became known as bushido. Guided by bushido, samurai developed strong fighting skills and faced their enemies fearlessly. Most importantly, they demonstrated great loyalty to their lords.

The code of the samurai became the standard of conduct for all Japanese in the mid-1800s. The Japanese sacrificed and lived for their emperor. This attitude led to fierce determination to win during World War II. The influence of bushido decreased after Japan was defeated.

PRACTICE

CALIFORNIA CONTENT
STANDARD 7.5.3

The Lord-Vassal System in Japan

DIRECTIONS: Choose the letter of the *best* answer.

1 **What was the basis of the lord-vassal system in Japan?**

A financial reward in exchange for land

B power in exchange for money

C military service in exchange for protection

D government positions in exchange for loyalty

"Never kill or wound a man in anger . . . When accusations are brought to you, always remember that there must be another side to the question."

—Hojo Shigetoki "Samurai's Instructions to His Son," from *A History of Japan to 1334,* edited by George Sansom.

2 **In the quotation, the samurai's advice to his son is to**

A react quickly in all situations.

B think before he acts.

C use his weapons skillfully.

D take control of every situation.

3 **How did bushido shape the culture of Japan?**

A Its ideals were forgotten under the military government.

B The samurai's loyalty to individual daimyo damaged Japan's national unity.

C The strictness of bushido discouraged young men from becoming samurai.

D It became the national code of conduct into the 20th century.

Name _____ Date _____

REVIEW

Buddhism in Japan

SPECIFIC OBJECTIVE: Trace the growth of distinctive forms of Japanese Buddhism.

Read the chart to answer questions on the next page.

Buddhism arrived in Japan in the sixth century. Different forms of Buddhism developed over the years.

Shingon

Shingon focuses on rituals that use the body, mind, and speech. Followers believe that saying certain phrases, using special hand motions and body positions, or concentrating hard will lead to enlightenment and help them reach the Buddha that is in all living things. Shingon Buddhists have influenced Japanese culture with their emphasis on beauty through painting, music, and gesture.

Nichiren

Many Japanese practice Nichiren. It was started in the 13th century by the Buddhist monk Nichiren. These Buddhists believe that the *Lotus Sutra,* a Buddhist text, contains the only truth. Devotion to it can lead to enlightenment. Nichiren was persecuted for his efforts to get rid of other forms of Buddhism. His followers split into several sects after his death. All claim to possess knowledge of true Buddhism.

Japanese Forms of Buddhism

Zen

Zen has strongly influenced the cultural development of Japan. Zen Buddhists believe that the ability to achieve enlightenment lies within everyone. Meditation and chanting can help lift a person to a level of enlightenment, which leads to peace, fearlessness, and spontaneity. Samurai favored Zen Buddhism. They attained inner peace and did better in battle. Artists were drawn to its simplicity, too. Zen Buddhists were also responsible for preserving and developing customs now tied to Japan, such as tea drinking, and types of art, literature, and theater.

Amida

This is a very popular form of Buddhism today. It is devoted to the Buddha of Infinite Light, who is called Amitabha. Followers believe that they will be reborn in paradise, the pure land, if they say the name of Amitabha devoutly.

Tendai

This form of Buddhism is based on the *Lotus Sutra*. It includes other practices as well, including meditation, the use of gestures, and chanting. Tendai monks were active in politics and were the founders of several other branches of Buddhism.

Name _____ Date _____

Buddhism in Japan

DIRECTIONS: Choose the letter of the *best* answer.

1 Why did several forms of Buddhism develop in Japan?

A The Japanese disliked the original form of Buddhism.

B The Japanese adopted forms that met with their needs.

C New forms were introduced each year from China.

D The government outlawed certain Buddhist practices.

2 Which Buddhist sects focus on the *Lotus Sutra*?

A Amida and Shingon

B Nichiren and Tendai

C Tendai and Shingon

D Zen and Nichiren

3 A major belief of the Amida sect is that

A wisdom can be achieved through the use of their bodies.

B only the *Lotus Sutra* contains the truth.

C all other forms of Buddhism are corrupt.

D an afterlife exists.

4 Zen Buddhists achieve enlightenment through

A performing complex ceremonies.

B studying and discussing texts.

C doing good deeds.

D raising their minds to a higher level.

5 Which qualities are associated with the practice of Zen Buddhism?

A ambition and creativity

B tranquility and freedom from fear

C ambition and inner peace

D simplicity and caution

6 In what way did Zen Buddhists contribute to Japan?

A They were actively involved in politics.

B As monk-soldiers, they helped to defend Japan in times of war.

C They influenced and preserved aspects of the Japanese culture.

D They trained all future rulers of Japan.

REVIEW

CALIFORNIA CONTENT STANDARD 7.5.6

Military Society and the Role of the Samurai

SPECIFIC OBJECTIVE: Analyze the rise of a military society in the late twelfth century and the role of the samurai in that society.

Read the information to answer questions on the next page.

Year	Military Government	Role of the Samurai
1192	Minamoto Yoritomo won control over the other daimyo. He established the Kamakura shogunate. A shogunate is the government of a hereditary military dictator. His government had many powers, although the emperor was still seen as the legal authority.	The samurai had the highest social status. They began to develop their own culture closely tied to Zen Buddhism. They became known for their military skills, their acceptance of duty, their courage, and their loyalty.
1274–1281	Mongols attempted to invade Japan. They were defeated because of the weather and the efforts of the samurai.	The samurai improved their methods of combat. The sword became the primary weapon of the samurai.
1338	The Ashikaga shogunate was established. It ruled for about a hundred years, but it began to lose power in the 1400s.	The samurai developed the customs thought of as typically Japanese. These included the tea-drinking ceremony and flower arranging, both a part of the Japanese culture today. A greater sense of bushido grew. The samurai held the virtues of bravery, honor and personal loyalty above life itself.
1500s	Under a weak Ashikaga shogunate, land-holding samurai fought among themselves in a series of civil wars.	The power of the samurai increased.
1603–1867	Tokugawa Ieyasu finished the process of unifying Japan. He established the Tokugawa shogunate, which ruled Japan for more than two hundred years.	The Tokugawa shogunate enforced a class system which the samurai were at the top. The samurai, however, had no real function because it was a period peace. As a result, many took jobs in the bureaucracy or in other occupations. The samurai culture initially flourished, but later, its simplicity could not compete with the attractions of the sophisticated city lifestyle. In addition, many of the samurai were on a fixed income and suffered economic hardship.

PRACTICE

CALIFORNIA CONTENT
STANDARD 7.5.6

Military Society and the Role of the Samurai

DIRECTIONS: Choose the letter of the *best* answer.

1 **What change in the samurai resulted from the establishment of the Kamakura shogunate?**

A Samurai loyalty began to shift to the shogun.

B Samurai fought more fiercely for their local lords.

C The samurai no longer needed to fight in battles.

D Samurai took on roles in the government.

2 **Why did the power of the samurai increase during the end of the Ashikaga shogunate?**

A They moved to the top of the social hierarchy.

B The authority of the central government declined.

C They developed their own culture.

D The bushido guided their conduct.

3 **In what way is a shogunate different from an imperial state?**

A Under a shogunate, the emperor has little real power.

B An imperial state has a strong army and navy.

C The bureaucracy controls all of the power in a shogunate.

D Rulers in an imperial state inherit their positions.

4 **During which age did the customs associated with the Japanese and samurai culture particularly flourish?**

A Ashikaga shogunate

B Kamakura shogunate

C Mongol invasions

D Tokugawa shogunate

5 **What was *one* major influence on the samurai culture?**

A their love of fighting

B their position in society

C Zen Buddhism

D Shintoism

6 **Why did the samurai enter other occupations during the Tokugawa shogunate?**

A The profession of samurai was outlawed.

B They wanted to extend their influence throughout society.

C They wanted to reach a higher level in society.

D The prolonged period of peace left them without a real purpose.

REVIEW

**CALIFORNIA CONTENT
STANDARD 7.6.1**

The Geography of Europe

SPECIFIC OBJECTIVE: Study the geography of the Europe and the Eurasian land mass, including its location, topography, waterways, vegetation, and climate and their relationship to ways of life in Medieval Europe.

Study the chart to answer questions on the next page.

Location of Europe
- Eurasia is the land mass that includes both Europe and Asia.
- Europe is about one-fifth the size of Eurasia.
- Europe is a peninsula in the western region of Eurasia.

Climate of Europe
- The climate varies in different regions.
- Northern Europe has cold winters.
- Southern Europe has mild winters and hot and sometimes dry summers.
- Rainfall is plentiful throughout the continent.

Vegetation of Europe
- Europe has farmland and forests.
- Agriculture varies, depending on the climate.
- Among the crops grown in Europe are grapes, olives, corn, rice, citrus fruits, grains, flax, sugar beets, and sunflower seeds.

Effects of Geography on Medieval Europe
- Rivers and bodies of water provided means of transportation as well as water and fish.
- Climate and fertile soil helped agriculture thrive.

PRACTICE

CALIFORNIA CONTENT
STANDARD 7.6.1

The Geography of Europe

DIRECTIONS: Choose the letter of the *best* answer.

Europe, 1000 A.D.

KINGDOM OF NORWAY
FINLAND
KINGDOM OF SWEDEN
IRELAND
North Sea
KINGDOM OF DENMARK
Baltic Sea
ENGLAND
ATLANTIC OCEAN
English Channel
Seine R.
Rhine R.
Elbe R.
Oder R.
Vistula R.
DUCHY OF POLAND
HOLY ROMAN EMPIRE
Loire R.
Danube R.
Bay of Biscay
FRANCE
KINGDOM OF BURGUNDY
Alps
Po R.
KINGDOM OF HUNGARY
KINGDOM OF LEON
Pyrenees
KINGDOM OF CROATIA
SERBIA
BULGARIA
Duero R.
CALIPHATE OF CORDOBA
Balearic Sea
Corsica
Apennines
Adriatic Sea
Iberian Peninsula
Sardinia
Tyrrhenian Sea
Sicily

National Borders
Rivers
Mountains

0   500 Miles
0   1,000 Kilometers

---

1 **According to the map, which statement is correct?**

   A The coastal regions have the highest elevation.

   B The entire continent of Europe is mostly flat.

   C The surface features include high mountains and low plains.

   D The Iberian Peninsula and England have similar land features.

2 **Which statement *best* summarizes the geography of Europe?**

   A Europe has numerous waterways and varied climate.

   B Europe has an extreme climate and harsh land forms.

   C Europe's climate and land features are uncommonly uniform.

   D Europe's geography has had little impact on its people.

REVIEW

CALIFORNIA CONTENT STANDARD 7.6.2

Growth of the Medieval Christian Church

SPECIFIC OBJECTIVE: Describe the spread of Christianity north of the Alps and the roles played by the early church and by monasteries in its diffusion after the fall of the western half of the Roman Empire.

Read the summary to answer questions on the next page.

Reasons for the Spread of Christianity

Church Leaders

• Various church leaders expanded the power and role of the Church.

• Gregory I, who became pope in 590, made his palace the center of the Roman government. He raised armies, repaired roads, helped the poor, and negotiated treaties with invaders.

Missionaries

• Before the fall of the western Roman Empire in 476, missionaries worked with neighboring Germanic and Celtic tribes.

• The converts ended up settling in lands once belonging to the empire.

Powerful Rulers

• Several Germanic rulers converted to Christianity.

• Clovis was the first Christian king of the Franks. By 511, he had extended his kingdom and Christianity over most of France.

• Charles Martel, ruler of the Franks in the early eighth century, expanded the Frankish kingdom. He helped to preserve Christianity in western Europe by defeating invading Muslims at the Battle of Tours in 732.

• Charlemagne became king in 771. His major land conquests reunited western Europe. He spread Christianity throughout his kingdom, often forcing his subjects to convert. Under his orders, monasteries set up schools to train future priests and monks. In 800, he was crowned Roman Emperor by the pope.

Monasteries

• The Church built religious communities for monks and nuns.

• Monks studied Christian works and made copies of the Bible and other religious texts.

PRACTICE

CALIFORNIA CONTENT
STANDARD 7.6.2

Growth of the Medieval Christian Church

DIRECTIONS: Choose the letter of the *best* answer.

1 The efforts of missionaries before the fall of the Roman Empire

  A prevented Rome from being overrun by invaders.

  B led to the conversion of Germanic leaders and people.

  C enabled Christians to escape persecution by the Romans.

  D helped Romans expand their political power.

2 Which statement about Medieval Christianity is *true*?

  A Christianity did not spread beyond the borders of Italy and France.

  B Most Europeans belonged to the Eastern Orthodox Church.

  C Christianity became a dividing force in Europe.

  D Christianity was firmly established in western Europe.

3 The Battle of Tours affected the spread of Christianity because it

  A kept the Muslims in the southern part of the Iberian Peninsula.

  B kept northern Italy and southern France Christian.

  C caused Russians to convert to Eastern Orthodoxy.

  D strengthened Islam along the North African coast.

4 Which factor probably contributed *most* to the spread of Christianity by the early 800s?

  A election of a new pope

  B establishment of monasteries

  C the growth of the Frankish empire

  D Germanic and Celtic converts

REVIEW

CALIFORNIA CONTENT STANDARD 7.6.3

Feudal Europe

SPECIFIC OBJECTIVE: Understand the development of feudalism, its role in the medieval European economy, the way in which it was influenced by physical geography, and how feudal relationships provided the foundation of political order.

Read the summary to answer questions on the next page.

The Development of Feudalism

Reasons Feudalism Developed

The death of Charlemagne led to the weakening of the Frankish kingdom. Lawlessness and disorder increased. Viking, Magyar, and Muslim invaders took advantage of Europe's weakness. They invaded the countryside and robbed the people. As a result, the people turned to local leaders for protection. Because kings were too weak to defend their regions, the feudal system developed.

Kings, Lords, Knights, and Serfs

Under the feudal system, kings gave land to powerful local lords. The lords became vassals of the king. In return for the land, they gave loyalty and military help to the king. The lords then divided their land among knights or lesser lords in return for military service. Peasants or serfs worked the land in exchange for housing, protection, and their own plot of land.

Manors

The manor, or lord's estate, became the feudal system's main economic unit. The geography of Europe meant that manors were able to produce most of what the people living there needed. Forests provided firewood and lumber. Rich soil and a good climate supported farming. Dairy products and leather goods came from livestock. As a result, few people ever needed to leave the manor.

The Growth of Trade

Powerful lords brought peace and stability to their regions. This led to the growth of trade. As trade developed, so did towns. At first, medieval towns were under the authority of feudal lords, who taxed trade. Townspeople then organized themselves to demand self-government. Guilds developed. These were organizations of individuals in the same business or occupation. Guilds soon became important economic and political forces in the towns.

Name _____   Date _____

CALIFORNIA CONTENT
STANDARD 7.6.3   *Feudal Europe*

DIRECTIONS: Choose the letter of the *best* answer.

1 In which group are the classes of feudal society listed in order of *descending* power?

   A king, lord, serf, knight

   B merchant, knight, lord, serf

   C king, lord, knight, serf

   D king, knight, guild member, serf

2 How did Europe's geography contribute to the development of the manor system?

   A High mountain ranges separated areas of Europe, dividing the land naturally into manors.

   B Plentiful natural resources allowed manors to be self-supporting.

   C Manors developed where numerous trade routes crossed.

   D Scarcity of farmland and water forced Europeans to band together on manors to survive.

3 What was *one* result of the feudal system?

   A increased regional interaction

   B great prosperity for the peasants

   C a return of order and security

   D a decline in Church power

4 How did early towns in Europe fit into the feudal system?

   A They were founded by feudal lords as a way to increase income.

   B Serfs lived in towns and worked on the manors.

   C Towns were begun and governed by guilds.

   D Most towns grew from trade and were independent of the manors.

REVIEW

CALIFORNIA CONTENT STANDARD 7.6.4

The Relationship Between the Church and State

SPECIFIC OBJECTIVE: Demonstrate an understanding of the conflict and cooperation between the Papacy and European monarchs.

Read the summary to answer questions on the next page.

Charlemagne

Early monarchs, such as Charlemagne, cooperated with the Church. Charlemagne spread Christianity throughout his kingdom. He also traveled to Rome to protect the pope from an angry mob. In gratitude, the pope crowned Charlemagne "Roman Emperor." This act created a link between the German states and the Church.

Cooperation between the Popes and Kings

During the Middle Ages, the role of the Church in the lives of the common people and rulers grew. All Christians had to follow canon law, the law of the Church. Punishment for disobeying Church law could be excommunication, which is banishment from the Church. The pope could also issue an interdict to control a king. This meant that sacraments and religious services could not be performed in his land.

When Otto I was crowned king of Germany in 936, he continued the pattern of cooperation with the pope. He even invaded Italian city-states on the pope's behalf. As a result, Otto became the emperor of the early Holy Roman Empire. Otto also established strong control over the Church in Germany. He chose the bishops and the heads of monasteries. This practice, known as lay investiture, became a problem later.

Conflict between the Popes and Kings

Later popes realized that lay investiture gave kings too much power. Pope Gregory VII put a stop to lay investiture in 1075. The German emperor, Henry IV, demanded that the pope resign. In response, the pope excommunicated Henry. Henry's bishops supported the pope. To save his throne, Henry stood barefoot in the snow for three days, begging to be forgiven. Finally, the pope gave in.

Conflict continued over this issue for many years. A compromise was reached in 1122. The pope would appoint the officials, but the emperor could veto them.

PRACTICE

CALIFORNIA CONTENT
STANDARD 7.6.4

The Relationship Between the Church and State

DIRECTIONS: Choose the letter of the *best* answer.

1 The pope crowned Charlemagne "Roman Emperor" because Charlemagne

   A gave money to the Church.

   B preserved the pope's safety.

   C spread Christianity throughout his kingdom.

   D was related to previous Roman emperors.

2 Why was an interdict an effective weapon for the pope to use against a monarch?

   A It banished the ruler from the Christian community.

   B It forced the king to give up his throne.

   C It allowed other kings to attack the king under the interdict.

   D It placed pressure on the king from his Christian subjects.

3 What did kings gain through lay investiture?

   A equal status with the pope in the Church

   B control over the Church in their kingdom

   C the pope's promise of eternal salvation

   D a large portion of Church income

"But from what you have since done . . . it is evident [clear] how little you care for our warnings, or for the observance of justice."

——Pope Gregory VII, letter to Henry IV, from Milton Viorst, *The Great Documents of Western Civilization*

4 With what action did the pope eventually follow up the warning letter to Henry IV quoted in the excerpt?

   A He visited Henry IV.

   B He approved Henry IV's bishop.

   C He excommunicated Henry IV.

   D He took over Henry IV's kingdom.

REVIEW

CALIFORNIA CONTENT STANDARD 7.6.5

Developments in English Law and Government

SPECIFIC OBJECTIVE: Know the significance of developments in medieval English legal and constitutional practices and their importance in the rise of modern democratic thought and representative institutions.

Read the summary to answer questions on the next page.

Independent Judiciaries

In 1166, Henry II began to appoint royal judges. They were sent to every part of the country to hear cases and make sure that the laws were the same throughout England. Although these judges were not independent from the royal government, they were unaffected by local politics. They were able to be fairer in their rulings. Their court decisions laid the foundation for English common law. Today, many countries have independent judiciaries, court systems independent from the rest of the government.

Habeas Corpus

Habeas corpus refers to the requirement for a person in custody to appear in court. Its purpose is to prevent unlawful imprisonment. Habeas corpus was probably first used in medieval England as way to protect personal liberty during the reign of Henry VII, 1485–1509.

Magna Carta

In 1215, English nobles forced King John to sign the Magna Carta. This charter guaranteed rights to the nobles, such as protection of the law and the right to trial by jury. It was also a step towards the idea of no taxation without representation. This document was an important first step in establishing legal rights for all people. It was a model for future democratic governments.

Parliament

In 1264, nobles removed Henry III from the throne. They replaced him with a parliament, a group made up of lords, church officials, and representatives from cities and towns. In 1295, Henry's successor, Edward, called two representatives from every town and knights from every county to be present. This became known as the Model Parliament. By the end of Edward's reign, parliament had become part of the English government. Parliament was important because it included non-nobles in the government and introduced representative government.

PRACTICE

CALIFORNIA CONTENT
STANDARD 7.6.5

Developments in English Law and Government

DIRECTIONS: Choose the letter of the *best* answer.

1 The appointment of royal judges was significant in the development of England's legal system because the judges

   A were independent of the king.

   B challenged the king's authority.

   C gave the king more control over his subjects.

   D were uninfluenced by local officials or customs.

2 Habeas corpus protects citizens against

   A illegal searches of their property.

   B losing their right to vote.

   C being held in jail unjustly.

   D trials without juries.

"To no one will we sell, to no one will we refuse or delay right or justice."

—from the Magna Carta

3 In the quotation from the Magna Carta, the nobles are making the point that

   A free men and women needed more rights.

   B not all witnesses in trials told the truth.

   C the laws were to be followed in all situations.

   D they deserved special rights and privileges.

4 How did the interpretation of the Magna Carta change over the years?

   A It was seen as a document that had historic value only.

   B It became the foundation for the law code in France.

   C It was used to defend the class system in England.

   D It was regarded as a guarantee of rights for all English citizens.

5 Which part of the United States government is like the English Parliament?

   A Supreme Court

   B the president

   C Congress

   D the Pentagon

REVIEW

CALIFORNIA CONTENT STANDARD 7.6.6

Causes and Effects of the Crusades

SPECIFIC OBJECTIVE: Discuss the causes and course of the religious Crusades and their effects on the Christian, Muslim, and Jewish populations in Europe, with emphasis on the increasing contact by Europeans with cultures of the Eastern Mediterranean world.

Read the summary to answer questions on the next page.

Details of the Crusades

Reasons for the Crusades

In 1093, the Byzantine emperor asked for help. The Muslim Turks had attacked the Holy Land of Palestine and taken over Jerusalem. People across Europe decided to support the Crusades. Some joined because Christian pilgrims could not visit the Holy Land. Some European kings and the Church also wanted to get rid of troublesome knights. Princes joined in, hoping to become famous. Merchants wanted trade routes to the East.

The Crusades

The First Crusade reached the Byzantine Empire in 1096 and captured key cities including Jerusalem. After their victory, the Crusaders divided the Holy Land into four states. When Muslim Turks recaptured one, a second Crusade returned in 1147. It was defeated at Damascus, but the Crusaders kept the other three states.

When the Muslim leader Saladin captured Jerusalem in 1189, the pope called for a third Crusade, led by Richard the Lion-Hearted. Saladin and Richard made a treaty. Muslims kept Jerusalem, but Christian pilgrims could travel there safely. When this truce failed, a fourth Crusade set off in 1202. It did not reach Palestine, but attacked Constantinople instead. Later Crusades had little effect.

Effects of the Crusades

The Crusades caused a shift in power in Europe. The failures of the Crusades weakened the pope's power. The feudal system also was weakened as many nobles did not return from the Crusades. This strengthened the position of kings. As trade with Asia developed, towns grew, and merchants became more powerful.

The Crusades led Europeans to think that all non-Christians were enemies. Christian persecution of Jews in Europe worsened.

PRACTICE

CALIFORNIA CONTENT
STANDARD 7.6.6

Causes and Effects of the Crusades

DIRECTIONS: Choose the letter of the *best* answer.

1 What was the cause of the Second Crusade?

A Muslim Turks had recaptured one of the Crusader states.

B Merchants wanted to open up new markets for trade.

C Jerusalem had been attacked by Muslims.

D Christian pilgrims wanted to visit Jerusalem.

2 What was the outcome of the Third Crusade?

A The Crusaders retook most of the Holy Land.

B The Crusaders were defeated by the Muslims.

C The Crusaders looted Constantinople and never arrived in the Holy Land.

D The Crusaders made a treaty with the Muslims.

3 How did the Crusades change the balance of power in Europe?

A The feudal system grew stronger, while the Church lost influence.

B Kings gained power due to the weakening of the feudal system.

C The Church more firmly exercised its control over monarchs.

D Many nobles who returned from Palestine entered the Church.

4 How did the Crusades change life in Europe?

A The population of towns fell.

B Trade was interrupted.

C Persecution of Jews grew worse.

D Kings lost power.

Name _____ Date _____

CALIFORNIA CONTENT STANDARD 7.6.7

The Bubonic Plague

SPECIFIC OBJECTIVE: Map the spread of the bubonic plague from Central Asia to China, the Middle East, and Europe and describe its impact on global population.

Read the text and study the map to answer questions on the next page.

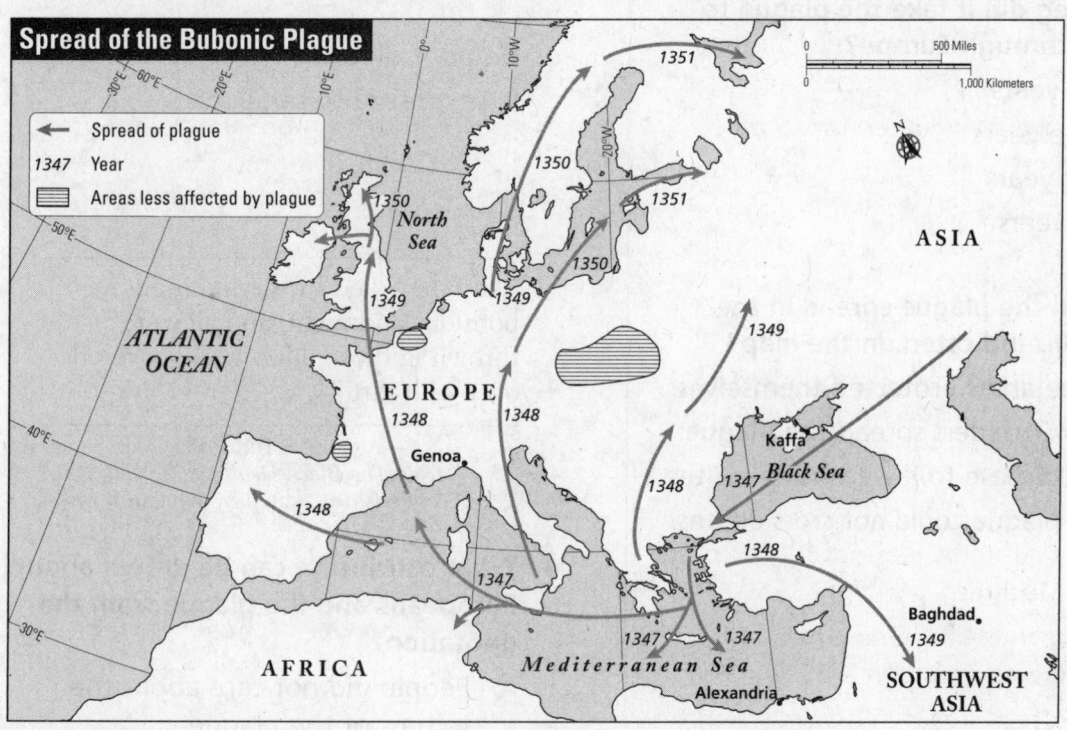

Spread of the Bubonic Plague

- → Spread of plague
- 1347 Year
- Areas less affected by plague

Spread of the Plague

The epidemic probably began in Asia. Infected rats traveled in the food supplies of trade caravans from China. Fleas from the infected rats bit people, giving them the disease. The plague spread in this way along trade routes to south Asia, southwest Asia, Africa, and then into the cities and countryside of Europe.

Effects of the Bubonic Plague

In western Europe, 20 to 25 million people, or about a third of the population, died. In China, India, and other parts of Asia, 25 million people died. Trade declined and prices rose. Serfs left the manors. Jews were blamed for the plague. They suffered persecution across Europe. The Church lost its influence because prayers did not stop the plague and some priests behaved in a cowardly way.

PRACTICE

CALIFORNIA CONTENT
STANDARD 7.6.7

The Bubonic Plague

DIRECTIONS: Choose the letter of the *best* answer.

Use the map on page 95 to answer questions 1 and 2.

1 How long did it take the plague to spread through Europe?

A two years

B three years

C four years

D ten years

2 Why did the plague spread in the directions indicated on the map?

A Some areas protected themselves.

B The Crusaders spread the plague.

C The disease followed trade routes.

D The plague could not cross oceans.

3 The plague was caused by

A the bite of an infected rat.

B the bite of a flea from an infected rat.

C poor diet.

D exposure to smallpox.

"And they died by the hundreds both day and night, and all were thrown in those ditches and covered over with dirt."

—Agnolo di Tura, "Plague in Siena" from *The Black Death, A Turning Point in History*, edited by William Bowsky.

4 What conclusion can be drawn about Europeans and the plague from the quotation?

A People did not care about the victims of the plague.

B Europeans never observed proper burial ceremonies.

C So many people died at once that they could not be buried properly.

D The plague was slow-acting and affected mostly the elderly.

REVIEW

CALIFORNIA CONTENT STANDARD 7.6.8

The Medieval Catholic Church

SPECIFIC OBJECTIVE: Understand the importance of the Catholic Church as a political, intellectual, and aesthetic institution.

Read the summary to answer questions on the next page.

The Catholic Church in the Middle Ages

Organization

The Church had a strict hierarchy. At the top was the pope, followed by cardinals, who helped run the Church. Bishops came next. They each supervised several parish churches. The priests ran local churches and gave the sacraments. The different leadership levels of the Church helped it to run efficiently and reach large numbers of people.

Political Role

Many higher-level Church officials came from noble families; others were educated with the aristocracy. Thus, the Church had ties to the ruling class. The great wealth of the Church made it powerful. The pope had more property and wealth than any king. As a result, the kings often cooperated with the pope.

Educational Function

Many religious orders were founded during the Middle Ages. These are groups of people who follow certain rules. Monastic orders live apart from society. During the Middle Ages, monks and nuns copied the Bible and other religious texts. Members of begging or mendicant orders were called friars. They lived by begging and taught the word of God as they traveled. Cathedral schools taught the sons of nobles. Students were taught in Latin and studied ancient Greek texts saved by Muslim scholars.

Theology

Greek philosophy emphasized the use of logic, a way of thinking using reason. Christian scholars wondered if logic and faith could exist together. In the mid-1200s, Thomas Aquinas argued that basic religious truths could be proven by logical argument. He wrote *Summa Theologica*, which combined ancient Greek and Christian thought.

PRACTICE

CALIFORNIA CONTENT
STANDARD 7.6.8

The Medieval Catholic Church

DIRECTIONS: Choose the letter of the *best* answer.

1 The organization of the Catholic Church helped it to

  A run local governments.

  B reach large numbers of people.

  C send missionaries to foreign places.

  D absorb the Eastern Orthodox faith.

2 What factor particularly increased the power of the Catholic Church over monarchs?

  A its hierarchy

  B the number of religious orders

  C the work of parish priests

  D the pope's wealth

3 What is *one* difference between monastic and mendicant orders?

  A Members of monastic orders devote their lives to God's service.

  B Monks perform their religious duties in society.

  C Friars depend on begging to keep their monasteries open.

  D Friars are largely responsible for preserving ancient texts.

4 How did Europeans gain access to ancient Greek works?

  A Greek scholars translated works written in ancient Arabic into English.

  B The works were preserved by Muslims and translated into Latin by Church scholars.

  C Merchants traveling to Greece found ancient manuscripts and returned to Europe with them.

  D Many Greek works were found hidden away in the libraries of monasteries.

5 Thomas Aquinas's work *Summa Theologica* was a historical landmark because it

  A dismissed the ideas of Greek philosophers.

  B showed Greek thought combined with Christian ideas.

  C increased the number of Catholics.

  D proved that logic was in conflict with faith.

REVIEW

**CALIFORNIA CONTENT
STANDARD 7.6.9**

The Reconquista

SPECIFIC OBJECTIVE: Know the history of the decline of Muslim rule in the Iberian Peninsula that culminated in the Reconquista and the rise of Spanish and Portuguese kingdoms.

Read the information to answer questions on the next page.

Time Period of the Reconquista

700s to 1000s

Muslims controlled most of the Iberian Peninsula. The Muslim culture flourished. Muslim and Jewish scholars worked side by side, making advances in medicine, astronomy, mathematics, and other branches of learning.

Small Christian kingdoms in the north began a 500-year military campaign to reconquer Muslim territories. Their goal was to bring them under Christian rule.

1100s

Muslim unity began to weaken. Different factions fought each other, leaving Al-Andalus open to Christian attacks.

1140

Portugal became a separate country.

1269

The Reconquista, the reconquest by Christian forces, was declared a success. Most of the Iberian Peninsula, except for the small southern state of Granada, was under Christian control.

1492

King Ferdinand and Queen Isabella achieved unification of Spain. They expelled all Jews and Muslims. They used the Inquisition to rid the country of all non-Christians. The Inquisition was a Church court that punished those who did not obey Church teachings. Prisoners were often tortured or sentenced to death.

Name _____ Date _____

The Reconquista

DIRECTIONS: Choose the letter of the *best* answer.

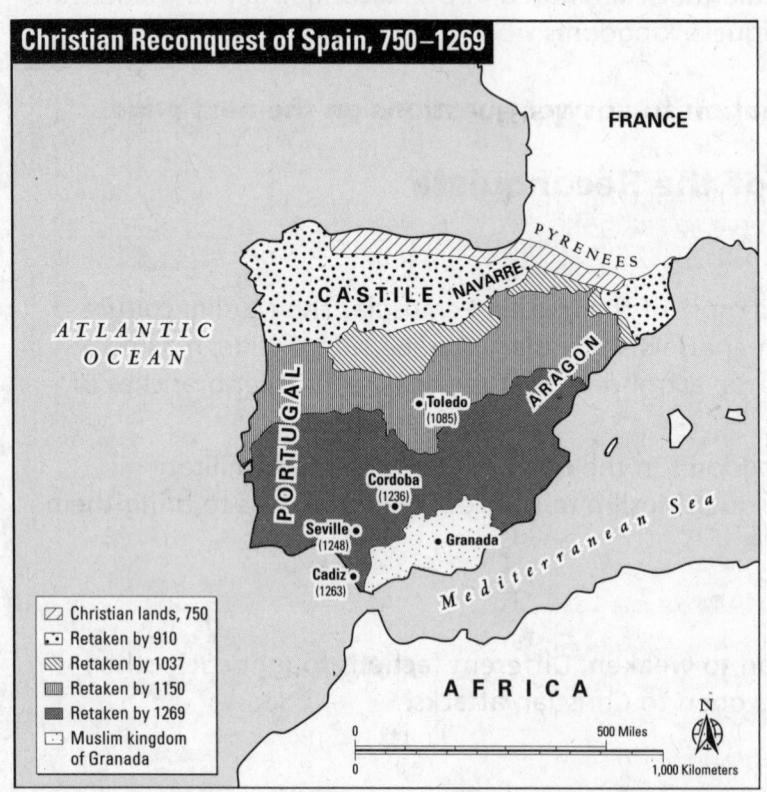

Christian Reconquest of Spain, 750–1269

FRANCE

PYRENEES

CASTILE NAVARRE

ATLANTIC OCEAN

PORTUGAL

ARAGON

Toledo (1085)

Cordoba (1236)

Seville (1248)

Granada

Cadiz (1263)

Mediterranean Sea

AFRICA

Christian lands, 750
Retaken by 910
Retaken by 1037
Retaken by 1150
Retaken by 1269
Muslim kingdom of Granada

0   500 Miles
0   1,000 Kilometers

N

Use the map to answer questions 1 and 2.

1 According to the map, which part of the Iberian Peninsula was under Christian control in the 8th century?

A the entire peninsula from the Pyrenees to Cadiz

B the part that became the country of Portugal

C a small area in the northern part of the peninsula

D Granada, Seville, Cadiz, Castile, and Aragon

2 According to the map, the Christians won back

A areas from south to north.

B the peninsula from west to east.

C the peninsula from north to south.

D coastal areas first.

3 In what way was Spain different after 1492?

A There was a policy of religious freedom.

B All Jews and Muslims had been expelled.

C It was a collection of small states.

D It included Portugal.

Name _____ Date _____

Geography and the Mayan, Aztec, and Incan Empires

SPECIFIC OBJECTIVE: Study the locations, landforms, and climates of Mexico, Central America, and South America and their effects on Mayan, Aztec, and Incan economies, trade, and development of urban societies.

Read the chart to answer questions on the next page.

Geography	Impact
Mayan Civilization (250–900)	
Location: The Mayan empire stretched from southern Mexico to northern Central America. **Landforms:** Lowlands are located in the north; the highlands are in the south. **Climate and Vegetation:** The lowlands include dry scrub forest and fertile rain forest. The mountainous region is cool and dry.	Farmers grew many crops. Terraces and irrigation canals increased land available for farming. This led to population growth and specialized labor. A class system developed. Cities grew from villages and became centers of religious ceremonies and trade.
Aztec Civilization (1200–1521)	
Location: The Aztecs built an empire in the Valley of Mexico in central Mexico. Their first site was on an island in the middle of a large lake. **Landforms:** The Valley of Mexico is a mountain basin 7,500 feet above sea level. It has several large, shallow lakes. **Climate and Vegetation:** The valley is fertile. A rainy season begins in May and ends in September.	Aztecs developed farming techniques that allowed them to raise crops on human-made islands. Tenochtitlán was the center of the empire. Bridges and causeways connected it to the mainland. The city had as many as 400,000 people by the early 1500s. They used trade to obtain goods they could not get locally.
Incan Civilization (1400–1532)	
Location: The center of the Incan empire was in a valley in the Andes Mountains. The empire extended along the west coast of South America. **Landforms:** The central Andes have mountains, valleys, and highland plateaus. **Climate and Vegetation:** Rain forest covers areas in the northern Andes. Fertile valleys between mountains are in the center. Elevation affects temperatures and land use.	The Inca terraced land and built irrigation systems to add farmland. They raised animals in higher elevations that were too cool and dry for crops. They built mountain roads, connecting parts of the empire. Runners called *chasquis* carried messages along the roads. Trade was limited to local and seasonal exchange. Lack of farmland and suitable sites prevented development of large urban centers.

PRACTICE

CALIFORNIA CONTENT STANDARD 7.7.1

Geography and the Mayan, Aztec, and Incan Empires

DIRECTIONS: Choose the letter of the *best* answer.

1 How did the location of the Mayan empire influence its development?

  A The Maya developed trade to compensate for poor land.

  B Fertile land led to farming surpluses and population growth.

  C Lack of level land restricted the growth of large cities.

  D The need to hunt and gather food kept Mayan society undeveloped.

2 How did the Aztecs adapt to the conditions of their first settlement in the middle of the lake?

  A They became hunters, not farmers.

  B They began a fishing industry.

  C They built islands to raise crops.

  D They raided neighboring groups.

3 What role did trade play in the Aztec civilization?

  A The Aztecs raised money by taxing all of the trade within their empire.

  B The Aztecs engaged in some local trade.

  C Trade was limited and controlled by the emperor.

  D The Aztecs developed a widespread trading network.

4 Where was the Incan empire located?

  A in the Andes along the west coast of South America

  B between southern Mexico and northern Central America

  C in central South America

  D along the coastal plains on the eastern edge of South America

5 Compared to that of the Aztec and Mayan cultures, Incan agriculture

  A was more successful.

  B used more sophisticated techniques, such as terracing.

  C depended more on the raising of animals.

  D was less limited by the environment.

6 Which statement characterizes the urban culture of Aztec, Mayan, and Incan civilizations?

  A All three civilizations encouraged the growth of large urban centers.

  B Urban centers were more important to the Inca than to the Aztec or Mayan cultures.

  C Compared to the cities of the Mayan and Incan civilizations, the Aztec cities were small.

  D In contrast to the Incas, the Mayas and the Aztecs had large urban centers.

Name _____ Date _____

SPECIFIC OBJECTIVE: Study the roles of people in each society, including class structures, family life, warfare, religious beliefs and practices, and slavery.

Read the summary to answer questions on the next page.

The Maya

• The four classes of society were the ruling class, the nobility, peasants, and slaves. The god-kings of each city-state and their families made up the ruling class. The nobles were scholars, architects, and merchants. The peasants included farmers and laborers. Slaves were prisoners of war or criminals.

• The Maya worshiped more than 160 gods, but they did not believe in a happy afterlife. Mayan rulers performed religious rituals in temples on top of pyramids.

• Kings sometimes declared war on neighboring city-states to gain control of trade routes or to get tribute.

The Aztecs

• Aztec society had three main classes. Within the highest noble class, the emperor was at the top, followed by government officials, large land-owners, military commanders, and priests. Merchants and artisans formed the middle class. The lowest class included farmers, fishers, and soldiers.

• Aztecs lived in family groups. Men farmed and women cared for the home and children. Boys learned about religion and were taught fighting skills.

• Most Aztec families had small altars in their homes. They believed in about 1,000 gods, mostly agricultural.

• Waging war was important. When taking a village, Aztecs would often kill everyone except warriors, who would become Aztec slaves.

The Inca

• There were two main classes. Nobles ran the government and the army. Commoners included farmers and artisans. There were no slaves.

• The Inca were led by a divine emperor, believed to be the son of Inti, the sun god. They built temples and held daily prayers and rituals.

• The Inca had a military force of almost 200,000 soldiers. Most soldiers were commoners who served a required period of time.

PRACTICE

CALIFORNIA CONTENT
STANDARD 7.7.2

Mesoamerican and Andean Societies

DIRECTIONS: Choose the letter of the *best* answer.

1 The slaves in Aztec and Mayan
society were mostly

  A children.

  B prisoners of war.

  C merchants.

  D women.

2 Which statement about the class
structure of *all three* societies
(Mayan, Aztec, and Incan) is *true*?

  A Nobles included the groups most
respected by each society.

  B Merchants belonged to the lowest
class in each society.

  C The ruler of each society was in a
class of his own.

  D Soldiers belonged to the highest
class of each society.

3 What did the religions of *all three*
cultures (Mayan, Aztec, and Incan)
have in common?

  A The three cultures worshiped Inti,
the god of the sun.

  B Each society worshiped many
gods.

  C Religion played a minor role in
the lives of their people.

  D All three groups looked forward
to a happy afterlife.

4 In what way were the governments
of the Maya and Inca similar?

  A They were both led by divine
rulers.

  B They both controlled most aspects
of people's lives.

  C Both governments included
elected representatives.

  D Both groups were ruled by
warrior-kings.

5 In the Incan tradition, military service
was

  A voluntary.

  B performed by slaves.

  C required of commoners.

  D a highly paid occupation.

REVIEW

CALIFORNIA CONTENT
STANDARD 7.7.3

The Rise and Fall of the Mesoamerican and Andean Empires

SPECIFIC OBJECTIVE: Explain how and where each empire arose and how the Aztec and Incan empires were defeated by the Spanish.

Read the summary to answer questions on the next page.

Maya History

1500 B.C.: The Maya began to establish villages in Mesoamerica.

A.D. 250: The Maya would build more than 40 cities and make important contributions in mathematics, science, architecture, and art.

700s: Warfare broke out among Maya. Food shortages resulted.

800s: The Maya abandoned many cities, leaving only a few weak city-states.

Aztec History

1200s: Aztecs arrived in the Valley of Mexico.

1325: Aztecs founded the city of Tenochtitlán.

1300s–1400s: Aztecs developed a thriving agricultural system. They made alliances with and conquered neighboring states.

1500s: The Aztec empire stretched from the Gulf of Mexico to the Pacific.

1502: Montezuma II came to power. His demands for tribute and victims for sacrifice led to rebellion within the empire.

1519: The Spanish arrived, led by Cortés. Fighting broke out and Montezuma was killed. Diseases such as smallpox weakened the Aztecs.

1521: The Spanish conquered Tenochtitlán.

Incan History

1100s: The Inca moved from the highlands to the valley of Cuzco.

1438: Pachacuti came to the throne. Under his rule, the empire expanded to include Peru and neighboring lands. This was accomplished by diplomacy and, when necessary, force.

1527: Civil war broke out in the empire, weakening it.

1532: The Spanish arrived under the leadership of Francisco Pizarro.

1530s–1570s: The steel weapons and horses enabled the Spanish to take control of the Incas.

1572: The last Incan emperor was defeated.

Name _____ Date _____

PRACTICE

CALIFORNIA CONTENT
STANDARD 7.7.3

The Rise and Fall of the Mesoamerican and Andean Empires

DIRECTIONS: Choose the letter of the *best* answer.

1 Why was the period from around A.D. 250 to A.D. 700 known as the Classical period in Mayan civilization?

  A During this time, the Maya were ruled by their greatest leaders.

  B It was the short period of time before the civilization declined.

  C It occurred at the same time as the classical age of ancient Greece.

  D Achievements during this period marked the height of Mayan civilization.

2 What contributed to the decline of the Mayan civilization?

  A loss of their urban centers

  B civil war

  C food shortages

  D conquest by the Spanish

3 What is one way that *both* the Aztecs and the Inca increased their territory?

  A They sent settlers to establish villages in unpopulated regions.

  B They made alliances with neighboring groups.

  C They purchased land from nearby city-states.

  D They forced regions to surrender by cutting off all trade.

4 Which leader's extreme demands for tribute and human sacrifice angered many of his subjects?

  A Pachacuti

  B Francisco Pizarro

  C Atahualpa

  D Montezuma II

5 In the decades before the arrival of the Spanish, the Aztecs and Inca

  A joined together to fight the Europeans.

  B were weakened by problems within their empires.

  C were involved in a war with each other.

  D sent out their own voyages of exploration.

6 The Spanish were able to defeat the Aztecs and the Inca because they had

  A shipbuilding knowledge.

  B superior weapons.

  C better maps.

  D better systems of communication.

Art and Architecture in Mesoamerican and Andean Civilizations

SPECIFIC OBJECTIVE: Describe the artistic and oral traditions and architecture in the three civilizations.

Read the summary to answer questions on the next page.

Mayan Civilization

The Maya built pyramids, temples, and palaces. The pyramids were built to allow priests to communicate with the gods. They had steps along the sides and temples on top. The Maya decorated the walls of temples and other buildings with murals. Skilled carvers created sculptures, made objects out of jade, and set up steles. Steles are pillars inscribed with symbols that record information.

The Maya's writing system had more than 800 hieroglyphic symbols. The Maya recorded much of their history and customs. The Popol Vuh is the Mayan story of creation.

The Aztec Civilization

The Aztecs built large structures. Tenochtitlán had many palaces, temples, and government buildings. The Great Temple in the center was a giant pyramid with two temples on top. The Aztec also made feather headdresses and jewelry with precious stones.

The Aztecs used pictures and symbols to represent words and ideas. Their glyphs were also collected in codices, folded sheets of bark or deerskin with colorful pictures.

The Incan Civilization

The Inca were great builders. They constructed more than 14,000 miles of road through the mountains. They built forts, palaces, and temples from huge blocks of stone without using any mortar. Some of their temples were heavily decorated with gold. Incan artisans also used gold to make jewelry. Their weavers used wool from alpacas to create cloth with complicated designs.

The Inca preserved facts and ideas through oral tradition and a *quipu*, a knotted string device that had symbols for numbers.

PRACTICE

CALIFORNIA CONTENT
STANDARD 7.7.4

Art and Architecture in Mesoamerican and Andean Civilizations

DIRECTIONS: Choose the letter of the *best* answer.

1 The pyramids built by the Maya were used as

   A astronomical observatories.

   B centers of government.

   C defensive structures in times of war.

   D the bases for their temples.

2 The glyphs of the Aztecs represented

   A the sounds of their language.

   B words and ideas.

   C religious concepts.

   D their family relationships.

3 Which statement accurately reflects *one* difference among the Aztecs, Maya, and Inca?

   A Unlike the Aztecs and Maya, the Inca concentrated on building an extensive network of roads.

   B Unlike the Inca and Maya, the Aztecs built large pyramids and temples.

   C Unlike the Aztecs, the Maya and Inca had an established written tradition.

   D Unlike the Aztecs and Maya, the Inca are not associated with building many large cities.

"Suddenly we found ourselves . . . in front of the ruins. . . . Made of beautiful white granite, the walls contained blocks . . . higher than a man. . . . I could scarcely believe my senses as I examined the larger blocks. . . . "

—Hiram Bingham, from
Lost City of the Incas

4 Based on the quotation, why was Bingham astonished as he examined the Incan ruins of Machu Pichu in 1911?

   A He was surprised that they were still in existence.

   B He was surprised that the blocks were made of white granite.

   C He was surprised that the Inca could move and use such huge blocks.

   D He was surprised that no one else had discovered these ruins first.

5 The Inca typically built their structures

   A at the foot of mountains and hills.

   B without mortar.

   C out of gold.

   D with the use of iron technology.

REVIEW

CALIFORNIA CONTENT STANDARD 7.7.5

Mesoamerican and Andean Achievements

SPECIFIC OBJECTIVE: Describe the Mesoamerican achievements in astronomy and mathematics, including the development of the calendar and the Mesoamerican knowledge of seasonal changes to the civilizations' agricultural systems.

Read the summary to answer questions on the next page.

Mayan Achievements

- The Maya believed that time was carried on the backs of various gods. These gods took turns. To identify the god for each day, the Maya developed a religious calendar. Depending on the god, some days were lucky and some were not.

- They also created a solar calendar based on their studies of the planets, sun, and moon. They calculated the year to be 365.2420 days. They were within 0.0002 of a day by today's estimation.

- The religious calendar had 260 days broken into 13 months. The solar calendar had 18 months, each with 20 days, and a separate period of 5 days at the end. The two calendars were used together to help the Maya determine the best time to plant crops, attack enemies, and crown rulers.

- The Maya invented zero, which enabled them to make precise calculations. They also had a number system with a base of 20 that helped them in their calendar and astronomical work.

Aztec Achievements

- The Aztec calendar system was based on the Mayan system.

- The Aztecs had two calendars. The sacred calendar had 13 months; the solar calendar had 18 months, each with 20 days. The separate 5-day period at the end was thought to be unlucky.

- Every 52 years, the two calendars would start on the same day. A ceremony marked the occasion.

Incan Achievements

- The Inca used a string device known as the quipu to record data. The knots and their positions on the strings represented numbers. The colors of the strings represented other information.

- The Inca are also believed to have had a calendar system with two calendars, one for day and one for night. These calendars were used for religious purposes. The Inca believed that gods ruled the day and time.

PRACTICE

CALIFORNIA CONTENT
STANDARD 7.7.5

Mesoamerican and Andean Achievements

DIRECTIONS: Choose the letter of the *best* answer.

1 Why was it important for the Maya to develop a religious calendar?

A to know which god was in charge of each day

B to avoid repeating the same ceremony twice

C to identify the course of the sun during the year

D to identify the lunar cycle, the cycle of the moon

2 Which statement about the development of the Mayan calendar is valid?

A The Maya relied upon Aztec knowledge to develop both their religious and their solar calendars.

B The Maya developed the religious and the solar calendars for political reasons.

C The Maya's invention of zero helped them to develop a precise solar calendar.

D Unlike other ancient peoples, the Maya studied the moon and sun to develop their calendar.

3 The Aztec solar calendar

A had thirteen months, each with 20 days.

B was identical to the religious calendar.

C included an unlucky 5-day period at the end of the year.

D had fewer days than the religious calendar.

4 The Aztecs celebrated every 52 years because

A they started a new religious calendar.

B both of their calendars started on the same day.

C there was an eclipse of the sun at that time.

D they had enough rain and very good harvests.

5 The Inca kept track of their numerical data with

A an abacus.

B a number system based on 20.

C the quipu.

D codices of data.

6 The *main* motivation for the Aztecs, Maya, and Inca to create calendar systems was

A economic.

B political.

C social.

D religious.

REVIEW

CALIFORNIA CONTENT
STANDARD 7.8.1

Humanism

SPECIFIC OBJECTIVE: Describe the way in which the revival of classical learning and the arts fostered a new interest in humanism.

Read the summary to answer questions on the next page.

Reasons for Growth of Humanism

- People wanted to enjoy life after having suffered through wars and the plague in the late Middle Ages.

- Increased trade in the 14th and 15th centuries introduced new ideas to the people in Europe.

- Ancient Greek and Latin texts became more available. As a result, interest in the classics grew. Scholars studied the classical works to learn more about the values of the ancient Greeks and Romans. Some of the qualities prized by the Greeks, such as order, harmony, balance, logic, and individual achievement, influenced the development of humanism and Renaissance values.

Humanism

- This revival of classical learning and other factors led to humanism, the intellectual movement that focuses on human potential and achievements.

- Humanism stressed the study of subjects such as history, grammar, literature, and philosophy.

- It emphasized the individual. In the Middle Ages, institutions such as the Church were more important than the people who belonged to them.

- Humanists tried to achieve a balance between intellect and faith. They felt that people should not accept blindly the teachings of the Church.

- Humanism also taught that people could enjoy life and still be good Christians.

Effects of Humanism

- Society adopted a more secular view. This meant that instead of the focus being on religion, it was on the things of the world.

- Important Church officials and wealthy merchants became patrons, or supporters, of the arts. They sponsored the creation of great works of art to bring glory to themselves.

- Artists and architects returned to the classical styles of the Greeks and Romans.

- The renewed interest in classical culture strengthened the Renaissance, which had already begun in Italy. The Renaissance was an explosion of creativity in the arts, literature, and thought from 1300 to 1600.

PRACTICE

CALIFORNIA CONTENT
STANDARD 7.8.1

Humanism

DIRECTIONS: Choose the letter of the *best* answer.

1 Why did scholars study the classics in the 14th and 15th centuries?

   A There were no medieval works to study.

   B They wanted to trace the development of Christianity.

   C They wanted to combine Greek and Christian views.

   D They wanted to learn more about the ancient Greeks and Romans.

2 Humanism is an intellectual movement that

   A emphasizes prayer and the Bible.

   B leads to happier lives.

   C encourages people to learn Latin and Greek.

   D focuses on the potential of humans to achieve.

3 What helped the growth of humanism during the 14th and 15th centuries?

   A Many Muslims moved from Africa to Europe.

   B People became interested in other religions.

   C Trade encouraged people to think in new ways.

   D People wanted to prepare themselves for death.

4 How did humanism try to balance intellect and faith?

   A Humanism encouraged people to think about Church teachings.

   B Humanism encouraged people to give up their faith.

   C Humanism encouraged people to sacrifice for the Church.

   D Humanism encouraged people to do what made them happy.

5 What style of architecture became common during the Renaissance?

   A Egyptian

   B Chinese

   C Arab

   D Roman

6 In what way did the Church show the influence of humanism beginning in the 14th century?

   A Church officials became less secular.

   B The Church changed all of its teachings.

   C Church officials became patrons of the arts.

   D The Church discontinued its collection of taxes.

Name _____ Date _____

Cities and the Spread of Renaissance Ideas

SPECIFIC OBJECTIVE: Explain the importance of Florence in the early stages of the Renaissance and the growth of independent trading cities, with emphasis on the cities' importance in the spread of Renaissance ideas.

Read the summary to answer questions on the next page.

Growth of Cities

For centuries, coastal Italian city-states had a monopoly on trade in their region, the Mediterranean Sea. Many trade routes from Asia to Europe passed through Italy. As a result, large cities developed, including Florence, Venice, and Milan in northern Italy.

Cities provided an ideal environment for exchanging ideas as well as goods. People lived close together and could meet to talk with each other. Merchants and travelers introduced new styles, attitudes, and views on life. These conditions helped cities become the location from which Renaissance ideas spread.

Within these cities, a wealthy merchant class formed. These merchants were involved in politics. They also had the time and money to pursue other interests, such as the arts. Many of these wealthy merchants became patrons. Their financial support allowed artists and writers to create great works.

Florence

Florence is located in northern Italy on the river Arno. Toward the end of the Middle Ages, Florence became a banking center, making it a wealthy city. Its population grew and included many artists and writers who helped shape the Renaissance. By the 1400s, the Medici family had assumed control of the city. Their dictatorship replaced republican rule. As rich bankers with great power, they were in a position to encourage the work of artists. The patronage of the Medici encouraged many of the great artists and architects to live and work in Florence. The Medicis were patrons of Leonardo da Vinci and Michaelangelo among others.

PRACTICE

CALIFORNIA CONTENT
STANDARD 7.8.2

Cities and the Spread of Renaissance Ideas

DIRECTIONS: Choose the letter of the *best* answer.

1 Which statement accurately describes the trading position of Italy?

  A Italy traded with northern Europe and Russia only.

  B Italy had major trade routes passing through it.

  C Italy did not participate in trade with the rest of Europe or Asia.

  D Trade led to the growth of small villages along the Italian coast.

2 Which condition helped spread Renaissance ideas?

  A feudal system

  B the growth of cities

  C knowledge of the classics

  D outbreak of the plague

3 What made Florence an early center of the Renaissance?

  A The city had great wealth.

  B It was on the Arno River.

  C It was strongly Catholic.

  D The city was very beautiful.

4 During the Renaissance, Florence was *most* noted for its

  A trade routes.

  B large churches.

  C fountains.

  D great artists.

5 What role did the Medici play in Renaissance Florence?

  A painted great artworks

  B were great writers

  C saved the government

  D patronized, or hired, artists

REVIEW

CALIFORNIA CONTENT
STANDARD 7.8.3

Marco Polo and the Silk Roads

SPECIFIC OBJECTIVE: Understand the effects of the reopening of the ancient "Silk Road" between Europe and China, including Marco Polo's travels and the location of his routes.

Read the summary to answer questions on the next page.

The Reopening of the Silk Roads

In 1260, Kublai Khan became the leader of the Mongols. Northern China already belonged to his kingdom. In 1279, Kublai Khan conquered the rest of China. The Mongols ruled China until 1368.

During Mongol rule, Asia enjoyed a period of peace and stability known as *Pax Mongolica.* Merchants and other travelers were guaranteed safe passage through the Mongol empire. As a result, trade increased between Europe and Asia. People felt secure enough to travel the Silk Roads again. These were ancient trade routes connecting China with Europe. They had become too dangerous to use with the decline of strong central governments, including the Roman Empire and the Tang Dynasty.

Among the increasing number of travelers on the Silk Roads was Marco Polo. His 24-year journey to China and back would have a major impact on Europe's relationship with Asia.

Marco Polo

Marco Polo was a trader from Venice. He and his father and uncle traveled the Silk Roads, arriving in China in 1275. There they made their way to the court of Kublai Khan. Kublai Khan welcomed foreign visitors to his court. He warmly received Marco Polo, who stayed in China for 17 years. During that time, he traveled to many cities in order to perform missions for Kublai Khan.

Marco Polo returned to Venice in 1295. Later, he was captured and imprisoned in a war between Venice and Genoa. While in prison, he told his fellow inmates about his adventures in China and what he had seen. He described how the government worked as well as many aspects of Chinese life. Another prisoner collected his tales into a book. This book became a best seller in Europe.

Many readers doubted the absolute truth of Marco Polo's stories. However, his journey increased people's interest in Asia and desire to trade with countries such as China. New ideas and goods from Asia began flowing into Europe, including Chinese inventions such as gunpowder.

PRACTICE

CALIFORNIA CONTENT
STANDARD 7.8.3

Marco Polo and the Silk Roads

DIRECTIONS: Choose the letter of the *best* answer.

1 What were the Silk Roads?

A areas in Asia that produced silk

B the Mongolian highways

C ancient trade routes connecting Asia and Europe

D sea routes that early Chinese explorers had mapped out

2 How did the collapse of the Roman Empire affect the Silk Roads?

A Pirates constantly raided ships in the Mediterranean Sea.

B Traffic on the roads throughout Italy increased.

C Travelers felt unsafe using the roads.

D The Byzantine Empire closed the roads.

3 What happened during the *Pax Mongolica?*

A Venice and Genoa reached a truce.

B The Silk Roads were not used by traders.

C Ideas from China began to reach Europe.

D The Mongols extended their empire into western Europe.

"More precious and costly wares [goods] are imported into Khan-balik [Beijing] than into any other city in the world. . . ."

—Marco Polo, *The Travels of Marco Polo*

4 Based on the quotation, what impression of China was created by Marco Polo's description of it?

A China was a country of great wealth.

B China was technologically more advanced than other countries.

C The Chinese were suspicious of foreigners.

D The Chinese system of government was efficient and fair.

5 How did Marco Polo's descriptions of China affect Europe?

A They inspired more people to learn to read.

B They discouraged others from undertaking the journey.

C They increased European eagerness to trade with China.

D They caused European leaders to restrict travel.

REVIEW

CALIFORNIA CONTENT
STANDARD 7.8.4

*New Ways of Spreading
Information (1300s–1600s)*

SPECIFIC OBJECTIVE: Describe the growth and effects of new ways of disseminating information.

Read the summary to answer questions on the next page.

During the Renaissance, several factors contributed to the growth in the number of people who had access to—and could read—books.

Paper Manufacturing

- Paper was first made in China in the second century from old rags, fishing nets, and fibers of mulberry and hemp. Before that, people wrote on parchment made from animals skins.

- China kept the secret of making paper for several centuries. Japan and Korea eventually learned the process. Then, in the 8th century, the technology spread to Baghdad and other places.

- Arabs improved papermaking techniques, using waste paper and old ropes. Paper manufacturing became a big business in the Islam empire.

- Muslims in the Iberian Peninsula established the first paper mill in 1056. From there, paper manufacturing spread to Italy and the rest of Europe.

- By the end of the 14th century, the price of paper had dropped 400%.

Printing Press

- The Chinese invented block printing. A block was carved with words or letters, inked, and then used to stamp paper. In 1045, China developed movable type, in which individual letters or characters are carved onto separate pieces of type. Because the Chinese writing system uses thousands of characters, this method was not practical for them.

- By the 1200s, block printing had reached Europe. European printers began to print whole pages with this process, but it was slow.

- In the 1450s, Johann Gutenberg of Germany invented a printing press with movable type. Now 500 books could be produced in 5 months, the same amount of time needed for one book to be copied by hand.

- In 1455, Gutenberg printed the Bible, the first full-sized book produced with movable type.

- By the 1500s, books were being printed quickly and in such quantity that many more people could afford them.

PRACTICE

CALIFORNIA CONTENT
STANDARD 7.8.4

New Ways of Spreading Information (1300s–1600s)

DIRECTIONS: Choose the letter of the _best_ answer.

1 Which list correctly orders—from earliest to latest—cultures that learned papermaking?

   A Japanese; Chinese; Arab

   B Chinese; European; Korean

   C Chinese; Arab; Japanese

   D Chinese; Arab; European

2 Which statement _best_ summarizes the importance of papermaking to Renaissance Europe?

   A Paper became cheaper and more widely available, allowing many books to be printed.

   B The manufacture of paper created jobs for many Europeans, who could then afford to buy books.

   C Paper mills introduced mass production, changing the economy of Europe forever.

   D More paper could be used by monks and nuns in monasteries when they copied books.

3 Why was movable type more useful in Europe than in China?

   A European paper was easier to print on.

   B European writing systems had far fewer characters than Chinese.

   C Europeans read text from left to right.

   D Europeans had fewer raw materials to make type blocks.

4 What was _one_ important effect of the printing press in Europe?

   A It led to the development of public libraries.

   B It enabled Gutenberg to become a patron of the arts.

   C It increased literacy as more people could read books.

   D It led to a renewed study of Latin and Greek.

5 How did the printing press contribute to the Renaissance?

   A Artists could mass produce their great works.

   B Literature became more important than art.

   C It led to a number of great inventions.

   D It spread Renaissance ideas to more people.

6 Once Bibles were printed in the vernacular, more people could

   A study Latin writers.

   B form their own interpretations.

   C become priests and nuns.

   D support the Church.

REVIEW

CALIFORNIA CONTENT STANDARD 7.8.5

Renaissance Achievements

SPECIFIC OBJECTIVE: Detail advances made in literature, the arts, science, mathematics, cartography, engineering, and the understanding of human anatomy and astronomy.

Read the summary to answer questions on the next page.

Literature

• Writers began to use the vernacular. More people could enjoy literature.

• Many authors in the Renaissance wrote to express themselves or to develop portraits of individuals. Modern writers still share these purposes.

The Arts

• Renaissance artists rejected medieval traditions. They did portray religious subjects, but realistically. Some subjects were from ancient Greece and Rome.

• They sculpted or painted important citizens, emphasizing individuality.

• They developed the technique known as perspective. Perspective allowed them to produce paintings that looked three-dimensional rather than flat.

Science, Engineering, and Mathematics

• Scholars advanced algebra by using letters in equations.

• Artists and scientists studied human anatomy. Scholars of this time made important discoveries, such as the function of the heart.

• Leonardo da Vinci sketched ideas for many inventions, including an aerial screw, the forerunner of the helicopter.

• Scientists developed new theories about the universe. They learned more about the minerals and metals that make up the surface of the earth.

• Architects designed huge domes for cathedrals using math calculations. Brunelleschi found a way to raise materials to the roofs of high buildings.

Cartography (Map Making)

• Advances in navigation, ship-building technology, and astronomy as well as longer voyages of exploration helped make maps more accurate.

• In the 16th century, Gerardus Mercator invented a way for navigators to plot a straight line on a map representing a curved surface. His projection helped sailors chart a more precise course.

Name _____   Date _____

**CALIFORNIA CONTENT
STANDARD 7.8.5**   *Renaissance Achievements*

DIRECTIONS: Choose the letter of the *best* answer.

1 **What characterizes many works of
Renaissance literature?**

   A use of Latin

   B suspenseful plots

   C focus on people as individuals

   D an emphasis on religion

"What a piece of work is a man, how
noble in reason, how infinite [endless]
in faculties [abilities], in form and
moving, how . . . admirable."

—William Shakespeare, *Hamlet*
(Act 2, Scene 2)

---

2 **What Renaissance value does the
quotation from *Hamlet* reflect?**

   A Humans were put on earth to
serve God and their king.

   B The potential of human beings is
limitless.

   C Most humans are weak and need
to be guided by authority.

   D Humans have little control over
their destinies.

3 **Renaissance artists tended to
produce works that**

   A were realistic.

   B were lacking in detail.

   C had dull colors.

   D resembled medieval art.

4 **The use of perspective allowed
artists to**

   A copyright their paintings,
drawings, and sculptures.

   B show the muscles under the skin
in their sculptures.

   C create the appearance of three
dimensions in their paintings.

   D apply layers of paint to create
color variations.

5 **The engineering achievement often
associated with the Renaissance is
the construction of**

   A thousands of miles of road.

   B elaborate tombs for popes.

   C huge domes on cathedrals.

   D bridges across many rivers.

6 ***One* factor contributing to the
increased accuracy of maps in the
Renaissance was**

   A greater knowledge about the
physical world.

   B discovery of ancient Greek and
Roman maps.

   C greater attention to detail by the
mapmakers.

   D greater availability of large sheets
of paper.

Name _____ Date _____

**CALIFORNIA CONTENT
STANDARD 7.9.1**

*The Catholic Church
in the 15th Century*

SPECIFIC OBJECTIVE: List the causes for the internal turmoil in and weakening of the Catholic church.

Read the summary to answer questions on the next page.

Factors Weakening the Catholic Church

Religious

- From 1378 to 1417, there was a split, or schism, in the Church. Two different popes claimed authority. One was located in Avignon, France. The other was in Rome, Italy. These rival popes caused confusion among the members of the Church.
- Many Church officials were seen as corrupt. They used Church funds to buy art or live extravagantly. Reformers criticized their lack of spiritual values.
- The sale of Indulgences angered many critics of the Church. An indulgence is a relaxation of earthly penalty for sin. By selling these pardons, the Church was making money. Also, many who bought indulgences wrongly believed that they were buying their way out of punishment in the afterlife.

Economic

- Europeans disliked paying taxes to the Church, especially when they did not agree with the way the money was used.
- Monarchs were jealous of the Church's wealth. They were angry about the fact that the Church did not pay any taxes to them on its property.

Social

- The Renaissance emphasis on secular values rather than spiritual values weakened the Church's authority.
- As a result of the printing press, people could read the Bible for themselves. They formed their own opinions and interpretations. Also, works that were critical of the Church were easily circulated.

Political

- The power of many monarchs grew during the Renaissance. As rulers grew stronger, they were less willing to accept the Church as being in charge.
- Leaders challenged the authority of the pope.

PRACTICE

The Catholic Church in the 15th Century

DIRECTIONS: Choose the letter of the *best* answer.

1 What was *one* result of the schism in the Church?

  A The Church doubled its membership.

  B The Church became more unified.

  C The Church's leadership was twice as effective.

  D Members of the Church did not know which pope to obey.

2 Critics of the Church disagreed with the selling of indulgences because

  A the priests had to spend too much time on the activity.

  B indulgences did not prevent people from sinning.

  C the practice did not bring in enough money to meet the expenses of the Church.

  D many people believed they would be saved if they bought indulgences.

3 Which statement *best* summarizes the shifting political balance in Europe during the Renaissance?

  A The pope and the heads of countries continued to cooperate.

  B The monarchs were supported by the wealth of the Church.

  C As monarchs grew stronger the pope became a figurehead.

  D Stronger monarchs disliked the pope's control.

4 How did Renaissance values affect the Church?

  A The Church grew as people became more devout.

  B The Church became less involved with politics.

  C People became more concerned with secular issues rather than religious issues.

  D The Church encouraged its members to question its teachings and think for themselves.

5 Why were many Europeans upset about paying taxes to the Church?

  A Paying taxes was a new practice.

  B They felt it was a sinful practice.

  C They disliked the Church tax collectors.

  D The Church did not pay taxes on its own property.

6 Many reformers criticized the Church because they felt that

  A church officials had lost sight of their true values.

  B the Church had become too bureaucratic.

  C religious orders spent all the money raised by the Church.

  D many of the bishops and priests were overly educated.

REVIEW

CALIFORNIA CONTENT STANDARD 7.9.2

Major Reformation Figures

SPECIFIC OBJECTIVE: Describe the theological, political, and economic ideas of the major figures during the Reformation.

Read the summary to answer questions on the next page.

The Reformation

The Reformation was a movement of opposition to the Church. As a result of the Reformation, the Catholic Church lost its authority over parts of Europe. New churches, known as Protestant, were started.

Desiderius Erasmus (1469–1536)

Erasmus, a Dutch priest, scholar, and humanist, was critical of the Church. He believed that the teachings needed to be purified and that many Church officials were corrupt. However, he wanted to reform the Church from within. He agreed with Martin Luther's ideas at first. Later he rejected them, feeling that Luther had gone too far.

Martin Luther (1483–1546)

In the 1400s, people could give the Church money as a way of lessening their punishment for sins. Martin Luther, a monk and a teacher, believed that this "selling of indulgences" was wrong. In 1517 Luther published his views in a list called the *Ninety-Five Theses*. These ideas were printed and spread throughout Europe, starting the Reformation. Luther believed that people won salvation through faith, not good works. The pope excommunicated Luther. By then, Lutherans had formed their own Protestant church.

John Calvin (1509–1564)

John Calvin developed a religion based on many of Luther's beliefs as well as his own. He believed in predestination, the idea that God decides before a person is born whether the person's soul will be saved. He established a theocracy in Geneva, Switzerland. Its religious leaders enforced strict rules. Calvinism spread in Europe and North America.

William Tyndale (1494–1536)

Englishman William Tyndale believed there should be an English version of the Bible. The Catholic Church was against this. Tyndale fled to Germany to do his translation. In 1536, before he could complete the Old Testament, Catholic authorities captured and executed him.

PRACTICE

CALIFORNIA CONTENT
STANDARD 7.9.2

Major Reformation Figures

DIRECTIONS: Choose the letter of the *best* answer.

1 What was Erasmus's approach to Church reform?

   A He believed that a total break with the Church was necessary to bring about reform.

   B He felt that reforms already undertaken by the Church were enough.

   C He supported Church officials but wanted to change Church teachings.

   D He wanted to solve the problems by working from within the Catholic Church.

2 Why did Martin Luther write his *Ninety-Five Theses*?

   A He was in despair over religious wars.

   B He was angry about his excommunication.

   C He was horrified over the sale of indulgences.

   D He disliked the lifestyle of Church officials.

3 *One* of Martin Luther's major beliefs during the Reformation was that

   A men and women are naturally sinful.

   B people should choose their faiths.

   C salvation required good works and faith.

   D priests were not needed to interpret the Bible.

4 What did John Calvin believe about the salvation of individuals?

   A People earned salvation by praying regularly.

   B People's salvation was decided before they were born.

   C People with strong faith would be saved.

   D People needed to help others in order to achieve salvation.

5 What kind of government did John Calvin support?

   A autocracy

   B democracy

   C monarchy

   D theocracy

6 To what cause did William Tyndale devote himself?

   A outlawing indulgences sold by the Catholic Church

   B setting up the English Protestant Church

   C writing an English translation of the Bible

   D fighting for the right of priests to marry

REVIEW

CALIFORNIA CONTENT
STANDARD 7.9.3

*Governing Practices of
Protestant Churches*

SPECIFIC OBJECTIVE: Explain Protestants' new practices of church self-government and the influence of those practices on the development of democratic practices and ideas of federalism.

Read the summary to answer questions on the next page.

Protestant Church Government

The Catholic Church had a strict hierarchy of authority. First came the pope, then the cardinals, followed by the bishops and, finally, the priests. Early Protestant churches, for the most part, did not recognize the authority of the pope or have cardinals or bishops. Church members were seen as equal in their ability to interpret the Bible themselves. This more democratic view of their membership influenced the governing practices of many Protestant churches.

For example, John Calvin established a presbytery in his churches. This was a group of church members and ministers who made decisions. In later congregational churches, the entire membership of the church shared authority. These approaches to church government were carried to North America by Protestants who settled in the English colonies. Their church experience shaped their attitude toward civil government.

The self-government of Protestant churches may also have set a precedent for the practice of federalism in the United States. Federalism is the sharing of power between a central authority and its members. The Constitution provides that while the federal government has some powers, the states have others.

The Mayflower Compact

The Puritans believed that God had made an agreement with people by which they could be saved. The Puritans applied this idea to their churches. People voluntarily came together to form a church. It was a short step to apply the same principle to government.

When the Pilgrims, a branch of the Puritans, arrived in North America, they drew up the *Mayflower Compact,* which agreed their government would make "equal and just laws."

PRACTICE

CALIFORNIA CONTENT STANDARD 7.9.3

Governing Practices of Protestant Churches

DIRECTIONS: Choose the letter of the *best* answer.

1 In what way did the Catholic and early Protestant hierarchies differ?

  A All early Protestant churches had bishops.

  B The Protestant churches did not recognize the authority of the pope.

  C The early Protestant churches adapted the hierarchy of the Catholic church.

  D All early Protestant churches were under the authority of the monarch.

2 What view shaped the approach of the early Protestants to their church government?

  A their opinion that priests could marry

  B the idea that they did not need a priest to interpret the Bible

  C a refusal to sell indulgences to church members

  D a belief that women should take leadership roles

3 What form of government was found in Calvinist churches?

  A Authority was shared among members of a presbytery.

  B The minister had complete authority.

  C The entire congregation made every decision.

  D All decisions were made by John Calvin.

4 Why was the early Protestant form of church government significant?

  A It had some democratic practices.

  B It became the model for all Protestant churches.

  C It was similar to the Catholic form of church government.

  D It was similar to the governments of European countries at the time.

5 Why was the *Mayflower Compact* an important historical document?

  A It set an example for freedom of religion in the United States.

  B It set an example for disregarding government charters.

  C It set an example for civil self-government.

  D All of North America was Protestant.

Name _____ Date _____

Religions in Europe and the Americas

SPECIFIC OBJECTIVE: Identify and locate the European regions that remained Catholic and those that became Protestant and explain how the division affected the distribution of religions in the New World.

Read the map and summary to answer questions on the next page.

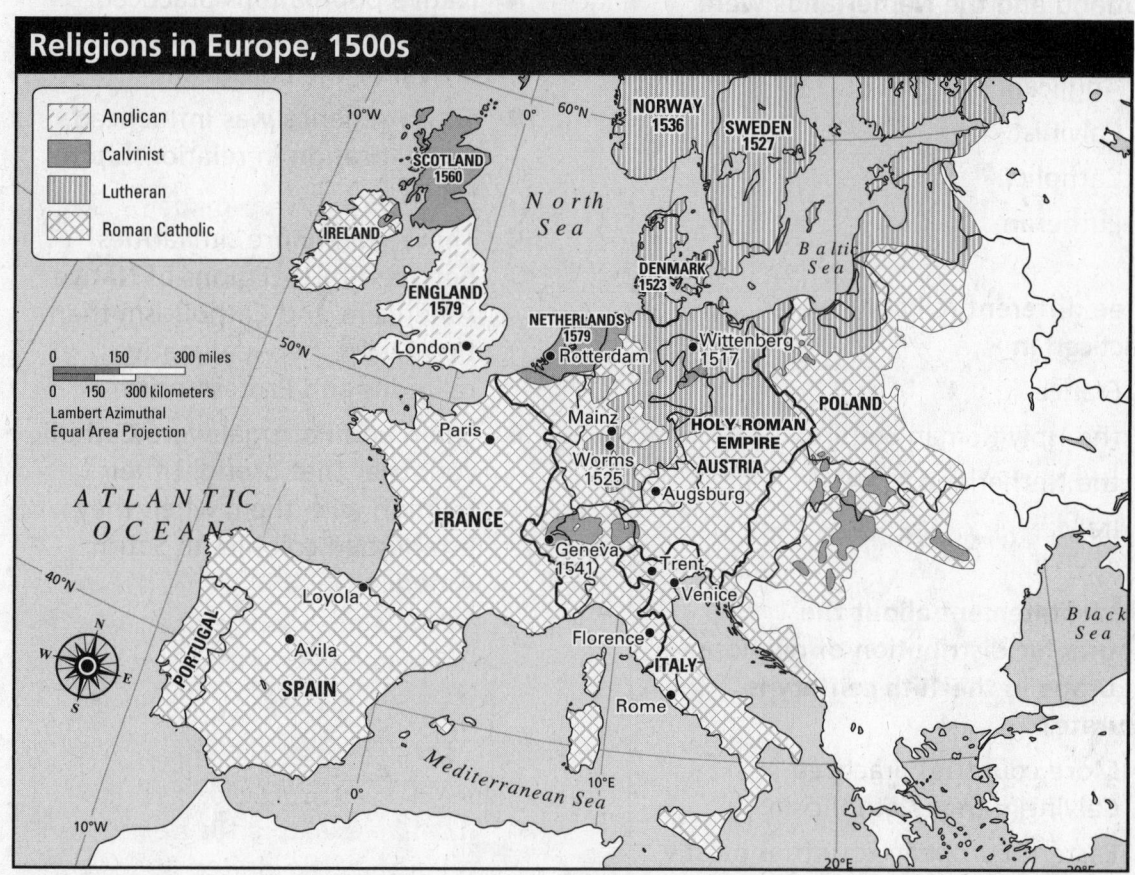

Religions in Europe, 1500s

Anglican
Calvinist
Lutheran
Roman Catholic

NORWAY 1536
SWEDEN 1527
SCOTLAND 1560
IRELAND
North Sea
Baltic Sea
DENMARK 1523
ENGLAND 1579
NETHERLANDS 1579
Wittenberg 1517
London
Rotterdam
POLAND
0 150 300 miles
0 150 300 kilometers
Lambert Azimuthal Equal Area Projection
Paris
Mainz
HOLY ROMAN EMPIRE
Worms 1525
AUSTRIA
Augsburg
ATLANTIC OCEAN
FRANCE
Geneva 1541
Trent
Venice
Loyola
Black Sea
PORTUGAL
Avila
Florence
SPAIN
ITALY
Rome
Mediterranean Sea
10°E
20°E

Distribution of Religions in the Americas

• While the Reformation was bringing about major religious changes in Europe, explorers were beginning to claim land in the Americas. The European settlers brought their religious beliefs with them.

• The Catholic countries of Spain, France, and Portugal established colonies in South America, Central America, and parts of North America.

• The English colonies in eastern North America were settled mostly by Protestant groups.

Name _____ Date _____

PRACTICE

CALIFORNIA CONTENT
STANDARD 7.9.4

Religions in Europe and the Americas

DIRECTIONS: Choose the letter of the *best* answer.

Use the map on page 127 to answer questions 1–3.

1 Scotland and the Netherlands were primarily

A Anglican.

B Calvinist.

C Catholic.

D Lutheran.

2 Three different religions were practiced in

A France.

B the Holy Roman Empire.

C the Netherlands.

D Italy.

3 Which statement about the geographic distribution of religions in Europe in the 16th century is accurate?

A More countries practiced Calvinism than Catholicism.

B Eastern European countries mostly adopted Anglicanism.

C Lutheran beliefs were strong in northern Europe.

D Calvinism was limited to areas around Geneva, Switzerland.

4 Why was Roman Catholicism the predominant religion in South America?

A Native populations practiced Roman Catholicism before the arrival of the Europeans.

B South America was influenced by its location in relationship to Rome.

C There were more similarities between the religions of Native Americans and Catholicism than there were between native religions and Protestantism.

D Spain and Portugal were Catholic countries that brought their religion with them when they established colonies in South America.

Copyright © McDougal Littell/Houghton Mifflin Company

128 CSS Specific Objective 7.9.4: Practice

REVIEW

**CALIFORNIA CONTENT
STANDARD 7.9.5**

The Counter Reformation

SPECIFIC OBJECTIVE: Analyze how the Counter Reformation revitalized the Catholic Church and the forces that fostered the movement.

Read the summary below to answer questions on the next page.

The Catholic Church took steps to reform its own policies and to try to stop the spread of Protestantism. This movement became known as the Counter Reformation or Catholic Reformation.

Measures of the Counter Reformation

- The pope called the Council of Trent. This was a group of cardinals who met from 1545 to 1563 to examine the policies of the Church. They wanted to reestablish the values of the Catholic Church. They also wanted to do away with abuses within it. They made the following decisions:

    1. The Church only was to interpret the Bible. Catholic individuals did not have this authority.
    2. Christians needed both faith and good works in order to earn salvation. Faith itself was not enough.
    3. Indulgences were valid. However, the false selling of indulgences was forbidden.

- The pope drew up a list of banned books and had them burned. These were books that he considered dangerous to the Catholic faith.

- New religious orders began. St. Ignatius of Loyola founded the Jesuits. They were a disciplined, well-educated group of religious people who did much to stop the spread of Protestantism. They started schools throughout Europe. Jesuit teachers had strong backgrounds in both classical studies and theology. The Jesuits also sent out missionaries all over the world to convert non-believers to Catholicism.

- The Catholic Church made use of the Inquisition. This was the court that investigated people suspected of not following the Catholic faith. This included Jews and Protestants. Its punishments were often severe and extremely cruel.

PRACTICE

CALIFORNIA CONTENT STANDARD 7.9.5

The Counter Reformation

DIRECTIONS: Choose the letter of the *best* answer.

1 What was the goal of the Counter Reformation?

  A to persecute non-Christians

  B to find ways to keep the Catholic faith strong

  C to show the advantages of the Protestant religion

  D to excommunicate Martin Luther and John Calvin

2 What was *one* reason for the Council of Trent?

  A to elect a new pope to lead the church

  B to draw up a list of dangerous books

  C to end some of the corrupt practices in the Catholic Church

  D to identify parts of the world to which missionaries should be sent

3 The Council of Trent stated that

  A the church and state should be separate.

  B bishops and priests could not forgive sinners.

  C Christians needed only faith for salvation.

  D the Church's interpretation of the Bible was final.

4 The Catholic Church authorized the use of the Inquisition in order to

  A increase the fairness of its laws.

  B educate people about its laws.

  C discourage the spread of Protestantism.

  D decide on valid interpretations of the Bible.

5 What was the Jesuit approach to stopping Protestantism?

  A They believed fear would keep Catholics faithful.

  B They felt that Protestantism could not be stopped in Europe.

  C They believed in educating young people.

  D They kept dangerous books away from Catholics.

6 Which factor may have helped the Counter Reformation to succeed?

  A the opposition of European Jews to the spread of Protestantism

  B the end of the Renaissance in Europe

  C the Catholic Church's strong and established organization

  D the decrease in popularity of the Protestant faith

Name _____ Date _____

Christian Missionaries

SPECIFIC OBJECTIVE: Understand the institution and impact of missionaries on Christianity and the diffusion of Christianity from Europe.

Read the summary and study the map to answer questions on the next page.

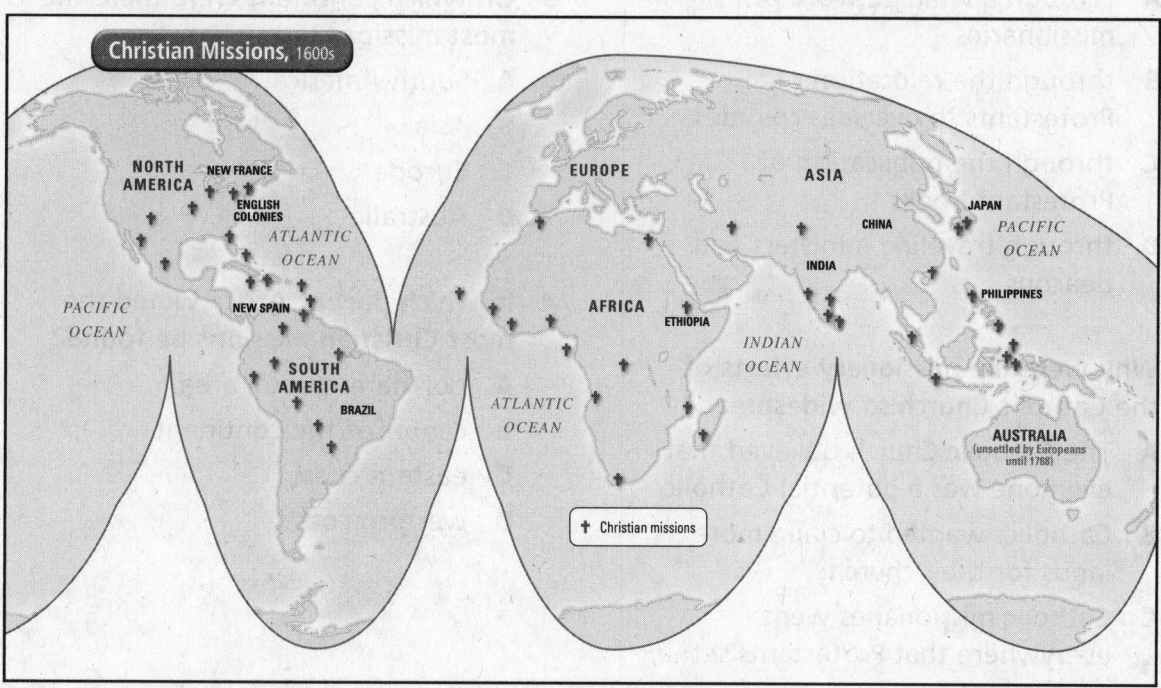

Christian Missions, 1600s

Missionaries

- Missionaries traveled to places to persuade people to adopt their religion.
- Both Catholics and Protestants wanted to spread Christianity to new lands.
- Catholics believed that anyone could convert to their faith. Therefore, Catholic missionary efforts were particularly widespread.
- Many Protestant churches believed that their members were chosen by God to be saved. Therefore, it was not their job to try to gather new members.
- Protestantism spread in North America mainly because European Protestants settled there.
- Catholic missionaries tried to convert Native Americans, who sometimes combined native beliefs and Catholicism. Catholicism soon dominated South and Central America.

Name _____   Date _____

PRACTICE

CALIFORNIA CONTENT
STANDARD 7.9.6

Christian Missionaries

DIRECTIONS: Choose the letter of the *best* answer.

1 In what way did Protestantism mostly spread outside of Europe in the 16th and 17th centuries?

A through a wide network of missionaries

B through the relocation of Protestants to overseas colonies

C through the publication of Protestant books

D through traveling ministers and deacons

2 Why were the missionary efforts of the Catholic Church so widespread?

A The Catholic Church believed that everyone was a potential Catholic.

B Catholics wanted to claim more lands for their church.

C Catholic missionaries went everywhere that Protestants set up missions.

D Catholic missionaries spoke many languages.

Use the map on page 131 to answer questions 3 and 4.

3 On which continent were there the most missions?

A South America

B Asia

C Europe

D Australia

4 In which part of Africa would the most Christian missions be found?

A northern coastal area

B center of the continent

C eastern coast

D western coast

Name _____ Date _____

Muslim Spain's Golden Age

SPECIFIC OBJECTIVE: Describe the Golden Age of cooperation between Jews and Muslims in medieval Spain.

Read the summary to answer questions on the next page.

Before the Muslims

From the time Jews first arrived in Spain, around 900 B.C., they were persecuted in various ways. In 612, the practice of Judaism was outlawed. Jews were forced to undergo baptism.

The Golden Age of Muslim Spain

Under the Muslim rulers in the eighth century, the Jews regained certain rights. They had to pay a special tax but were allowed to practice their religion. They had their own living areas, governed themselves, and had their own court system.

Together, Muslim and Jewish scholars contributed to a golden age of learning in Spain. Jews served as government officials or advisors to Muslim rulers. They translated Arabic texts into romance languages and Greek and Hebrew texts into Arabic. A Jewish physician, Hasdai ben Shaprut, served as the Muslim ruler's doctor. An important philosopher was the Jewish scholar Moses Maimonides.

Some Jewish and Muslim practices became mingled. Arabic was used for Jewish prayers. Jews often wore Muslim clothing styles and washed their feet and hands before entering their synagogues.

The Spanish Inquisition

Unfortunately, by the 12th century, life became more difficult for the Jews. First the Almoravides gained power in the 11th century. These were more extreme Muslims, less tolerant of other faiths. Then the Almohads took over. Jews still worked as cobblers, moneylenders, jewelers, and tailors. However, they had to wear identifying clothing such as yellow turbans.

As Christians conquered more of Spain, conditions worsened for the Jews. They were often forced to convert to Christianity. Anti-Jewish riots took place in several cities. Then the Spanish Inquisition began. Many Jews suffered torture and death. Finally, all Jews—about 100,000—were expelled from Spain in 1492.

PRACTICE

CALIFORNIA CONTENT
STANDARD 7.9.7

Muslim Spain's Golden Age

DIRECTIONS: Choose the letter of the *best* answer.

1 Which statement describes the treatment of the Jews in Spain before the arrival of the Muslims?

A Jews enjoyed equal privileges with Christians.

B Jews constantly lived in fear of death.

C Jews' rights and privileges were restricted, often severely.

D Jews controlled government offices.

2 In Muslim Spain, what did the Jewish status as "people of the book" mean?

A They were forced to convert to Islam.

B They had to pay a tax but could practice their religion.

C They could not leave the part of town designated as Jewish.

D They received the same treatment as Muslims in Muslim Spain.

3 Why was the Jewish presence in Muslim Spain significant?

A Jews contributed greatly to the scholarship of the time.

B Jews in several large cities caused civil unrest.

C Jews kept the Christians from taking over Muslim Spain.

D Jews succeeded in converting many Muslims to the Jewish faith.

4 The relationship between the Muslims and Jews during the golden age of Spain might be described as

A uneasy and frustrating.

B cooperative and productive.

C competitive and bitter.

D distant but respectful.

5 What ended the golden age of Spain?

A conquest by extreme sects of Muslims and then Christians

B the expulsion of Muslims from Spain

C the Christian Crusades to the holy land

D the collapse of the economy and urban centers of learning

6 What occurred in the 15th century in Spain?

A Under Christian rulers, a new golden age of arts and learning began.

B A more moderate Muslim sect reestablished control and restored order.

C Jews regained some limited rights and status under new Christian rulers.

D Christian rulers began the Inquisition and forced all Jews out of the country.

REVIEW

**CALIFORNIA CONTENT
STANDARD 7.10.1**

The Scientific Revolution
(1500s–1700s)

SPECIFIC OBJECTIVE: Discuss the roots of the Scientific Revolution.

Read the summary to answer questions on the next page.

Roots of the Scientific Revolution

Greek Rationalism

Ancient Greek thinkers used reason and logic to explain how the world
worked. As a result, the Greeks made many discoveries. Euclid and
Pythagoras developed geometry, and Galen discovered that veins were
filled with blood, not air.

Jewish, Christian, and Muslim Science

During the Middle Ages, Islamic and Jewish scholars, kept the knowledge
from earlier civilizations safe. They built upon that knowledge. Muslims
developed algebra and a medical encyclopedia that was used for
hundreds of years. Gersonides, a Jewish astronomer, proved that stars
were far from Earth. Muslim and Jewish scholars translated works from
Greek and Arabic into Latin, so Europeans could read them.

Renaissance Humanism

Works of Greek thinkers became more widely available during the
Renaissance. As a result, Europeans learned how Greeks used reason
and logic to solve problems. Soon Europeans also began to question old
ideas. European scholars questioned which ideas were true and which
were false. They became bolder in their search for knowledge.

Global Exploration

During the Renaissance, explorers reached lands unknown to Europeans.
The new peoples, vegetation, and animals made Europeans realize how
much they had yet to discover.

The Scientific Revolution

These influences led to a new way of looking at the natural world.
Scholars questioned old scientific ideas and Christian beliefs. The
Scientific Revolution, a time of brilliant discoveries, resulted.

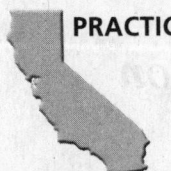

PRACTICE

CALIFORNIA CONTENT
STANDARD 7.10.1

The Scientific Revolution (1500s–1700s)

DIRECTIONS: Choose the letter of the *best* answer.

1 What role did the Muslim world play in the Scientific Revolution?

A Knowledge passed from the Muslim world to European thinkers.

B Muslim scientists focused on great discoveries in the fields of navigation and architecture.

C Trade between the Muslim world and Europe helped finance scientific efforts.

D The Muslim world had little influence on the Scientific Revolution.

2 As ancient Greek texts became more widely read, European thinkers found out that

A there was little left to learn about science.

B the world had changed greatly since the ancient Greeks.

C there were different opinions about some important ideas.

D the Greeks were not as advanced as had been previously thought.

3 How did Renaissance values affect the Scientific Revolution?

A During the Renaissance, people focused on reforming the Catholic Church.

B The Renaissance thinking only changed art, architecture, and literature.

C The Renaissance desire to enjoy life decreased the attention paid to serious scholarship.

D The Renaissance spirit of investigation led scholars to make important discoveries.

4 What was *one* thing Europeans realized as a result of increased exploration?

A that the earth was the center of the universe

B that they had much left to discover about the world

C that reason could solve all problems

D that the risks of exploration outweighed its benefits

Name _____ Date _____

REVIEW

**CALIFORNIA CONTENT
STANDARD 7.10.2**

New Scientific Theories and Inventions

SPECIFIC OBJECTIVE: Understand the significance of the new scientific theories and the significance of new inventions.

Read the time line to answer questions on the next page.

Important Theories and Invention

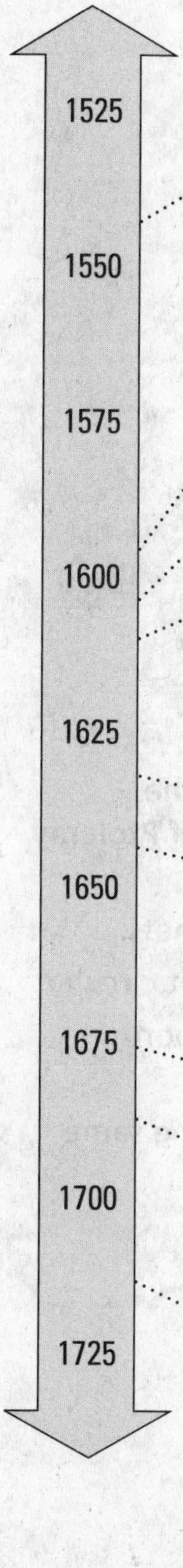 1525	**1543:** Nicolaus Copernicus stated that Earth, stars, and planets moved around the sun. This contradicted the accepted view that the earth was the center of the universe and did not please the Church.
1550	**1590:** Zacharias Janssen invented the microscope.
1575	**1609:** Johannes Kepler proved Copernicus's theory by using mathematical laws. He also showed that the planets had oval orbits, not circular ones.
1600	**1610:** Galileo Galilei used the telescope to study the heavens. He found that the sun and moon were not made of a pure and perfect substance as Aristotle had believed.
1625	**1628:** William Harvey showed that blood was pumped through the body by the heart, not the liver as the Greeks believed.
1650	**1643:** Evangelista Torricelli invented the barometer, which measured the pressure of Earth's atmosphere. Later scientists used the barometer to predict the weather.
1675	**1670s:** Anton von Leeuwenhoek used the microscope to observe bacteria.
1700	**1687:** Isaac Newton's theory of motion stated that all objects in the universe were affected by gravity. This force kept planets in their orbits.
1725	**1714:** Gabriel Fahrenheit invented the first mercury thermometer. He also developed a temperature scale.

PRACTICE

**CALIFORNIA CONTENT
STANDARD 7.10.2**

New Scientific Theories
and Inventions

DIRECTIONS: Choose the letter of the *best* answer.

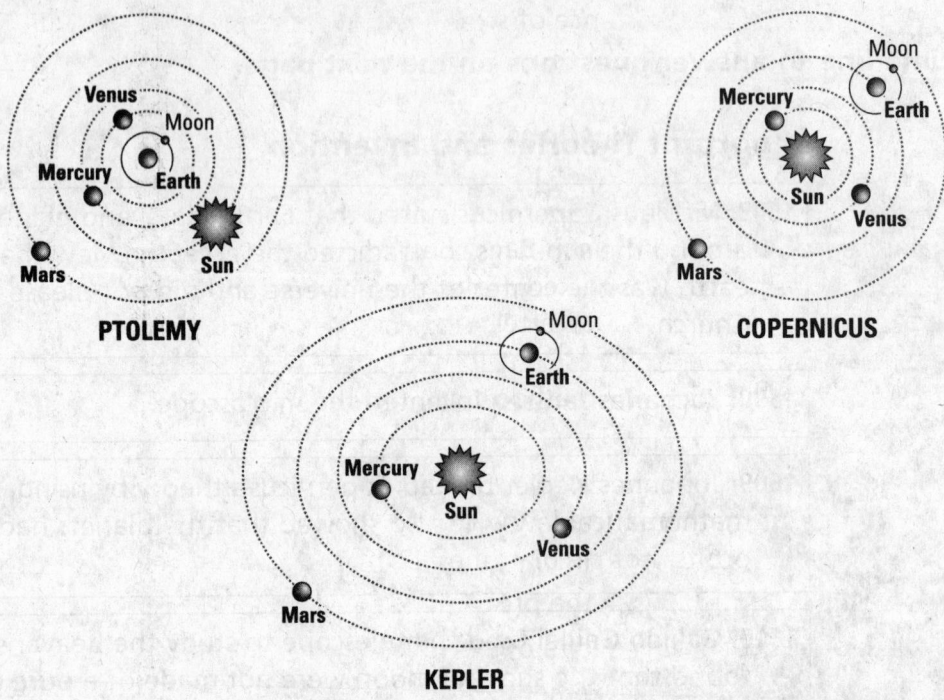

PTOLEMY

COPERNICUS

KEPLER

Use the diagram to answer questions 1 and 2.

1 How did Copernicus's view of the universe differ from Ptolemy's?

  A Copernicus placed Mars closer to Earth.

  B Ptolemy did not identify Venus or Mercury.

  C Copernicus had the planets revolving around the sun.

  D Ptolemy ignored the moon as well as Mars.

2 How did Kepler's view of the universe differ from that of Ptolemy and Copernicus?

  A He identified more planets.

  B His orbits were oval, not circular.

  C He did not have the moon orbiting Earth.

  D He placed Mercury in the same orbit as Earth.

Name _____ Date _____

REVIEW

CALIFORNIA CONTENT STANDARD 7.10.3 *Scientific Rationalism*

SPECIFIC OBJECTIVE: Understand the scientific method advanced by Bacon and Descartes, the influence of new scientific rationalism on the growth of democratic ideas, and the coexistence of science with traditional religious beliefs.

Read the summary to answer questions on the next page.

Francis Bacon and René Descartes

Seventeenth-century philosophers Francis Bacon and René Descartes both thought that past beliefs should be rejected. However, they had different ways of gathering new knowledge. Descartes used reason, while Bacon used experimentation. Both approaches contributed to the development of what became known as the scientific method.

The Scientific Method

The scientific method, developed in the 17th century, is still used by scientists today. It has four major steps.

1. Make observations to determine the problem.
2. Form a hypothesis, an unproven idea of what the answer might be.
3. Test the hypothesis through experiments.
4. Use reason to analyze the results. Then draw a conclusion that either supports the hypothesis or proves it wrong.

Impact of Scientific Rationalism on the Church

During the Middle Ages, people relied on the Church to provide answers to many puzzling questions about their world. When people began to find some of these answers for themselves, they became less dependent on the Church. Some scientific investigations did not agree with the Church's teachings. This began to weaken the Church's authority.

Other Effects of Scientific Rationalism

Some political thinkers applied scientific rationalism to find natural laws. These laws changed their views on government. For example, John Locke believed that people had the right to control their own lives. This idea supported democratic forms of government.

PRACTICE

CALIFORNIA CONTENT
STANDARD 7.10.3

Scientific Rationalism

DIRECTIONS: Choose the letter of the *best* answer.

1 René Descartes and Francis Bacon differed in their

  A view that all previous beliefs should be questioned.

  B approach to gathering scientific knowledge.

  C interest in finding new scientific facts.

  D ideas about the importance of scientific rationalism.

2 In what way did scientific rationalism affect the Church?

  A The authority of the Church became stronger as people realized the limitations of reason.

  B People's belief in their ability to think for themselves decreased the power of the Church.

  C The Church applied the principles of scientific rationalism to its policies and made changes.

  D The authority of the Church was unaffected by the ideas of scientific rationalism.

3 The influence of scientific rationalism eventually led people to

  A rely more on the ancient ideas of the Greeks and Romans.

  B reject the new scientific theories of Bacon and Descartes.

  C question traditional beliefs in areas other than science.

  D enter the field of scientific research.

4 How did scientific rationalism affect political thought?

  A It led directly to new democratic governments across Europe.

  B Rationalism reinforced the need for strong monarchs.

  C Some political thinkers began to look for alternative forms of government.

  D Most political thinkers were unaffected by scientific rationalism.

Name _____   Date _____

The Age of Exploration

SPECIFIC OBJECTIVE: Know the great voyages of discovery, the locations of the routes, and the influence of cartography on the development of a new European worldview.

Study the summary and the map to answer questions on the next page.

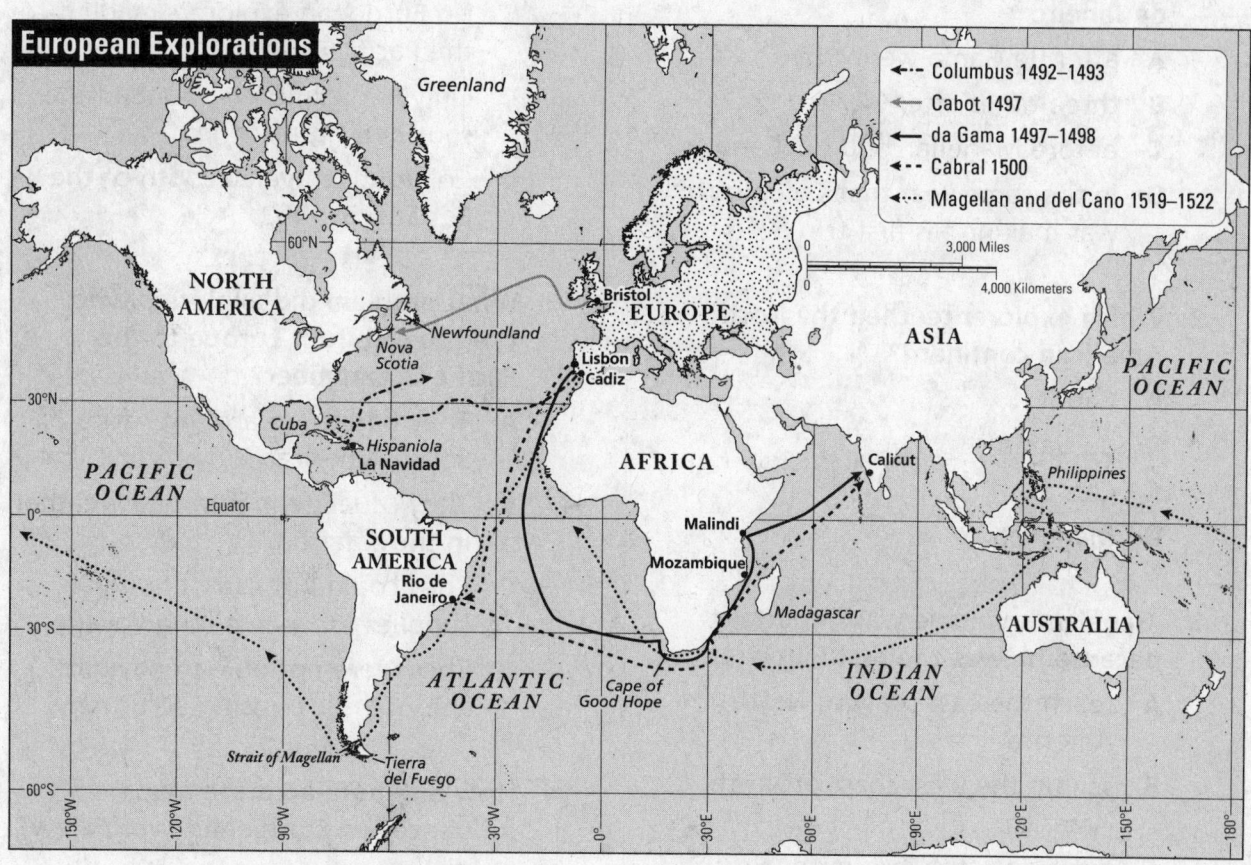

European Explorations

- Columbus 1492–1493
- Cabot 1497
- da Gama 1497–1498
- Cabral 1500
- Magellan and del Cano 1519–1522

- By the 1500s, maps became increasingly accurate. Each voyage added to the Europeans' understanding of the world.

- Maps showed the continents of North and South America. These continents were named after the explorer Amerigo Vespucci. He was one of the first to map the coasts of these lands.

- As a result of better maps and more information, Europeans broadened their worldview to include the western continents and the Spice Islands in the east.

Name _____ Date _____

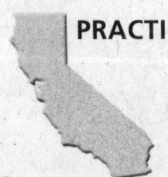
DIRECTIONS: Choose the letter of the *best* answer.

Use the map on page 141 to answer questions 1–5.

1 Cabral traveled to what is now Rio de Janeiro

   A after de Gama went there.

   B three times after 1492.

   C before Magellan and del Cano.

   D in the same year that Columbus was making his first trip overseas.

2 Which explorer reached the North American continent?

   A Cabot

   B da Gama

   C Cabral

   D Magellan

3 Magellan's voyage was important because he was the first European to

   A reach the east coast of North America.

   B sail up the west coast of North America.

   C travel into the interior of North America.

   D sail all the way around the world.

4 Which statement accurately reflects information shown on the map?

   A Several voyages originated in Lisbon and Cadiz.

   B No European explorers made it to the Pacific Ocean.

   C Only two explorers rounded the southern tip of Africa.

   D Columbus traveled south of the Equator in 1493.

5 What problem did explorers who tried to sail from Europe to the Pacific Ocean meet?

   A They had to go around Africa or South America.

   B They usually ran into bad weather in the Atlantic.

   C They could not carry enough supplies for such a long voyage.

   D They were not able to navigate the Atlantic crossing accurately.

6 How did more accurate maps influence the Europeans' worldview?

   A Europeans focused on the area around the Mediterranean.

   B Europeans included the Americas and lands to the east.

   C Europeans broadened their view to include lands further east.

   D Europeans narrowed their focus to North and South America.

Name _____ Date _____

REVIEW

CALIFORNIA CONTENT STANDARD 7.11.2

The Columbian Exchange

SPECIFIC OBJECTIVE: Discuss the exchanges of plants, animals, technology, culture, and ideas among Europe, Africa, Asia, and the Americas in the 15th and 16th centuries and the major economic and social effects on each continent.

Read the chart below to answer questions on the next page.

On their trips to and from the Americas, Europeans moved many goods. This transfer became known as the Columbian Exchange. It had social and economic effects in the Western and Eastern Hemispheres.

From Europe, Asia, Africa to the Americas
- Livestock: horses, cattle, sheep, pigs
- Fruits and vegetables: bananas, black-eyed peas, yams, olives, citrus fruits, grapes, peaches, pears, turnips, onions
- Grains: wheat, rice, barley, oats
- Other crops: coffee beans, sugar cane
- Diseases: smallpox, measles, influenza
- Belief systems: Christianity

From the Americas to Europe, Asia, and Africa
- Animals: turkeys
- Vegetables: squash, pumpkins, sweet potatoes, peppers, avocados, potatoes, tomatoes, corn, beans
- Fruits: pineapples
- Other crops: cacao beans, quinine, tobacco

Impact on the Americas
- New patterns of international trade began.
- Many Native Americans were converted to Christianity.
- Disease claimed the lives of over 20 million Native Americans.
- New methods of agriculture resulted from the introduction of livestock and different crops.
- Horses improved transportation.

Impact on Europe, Asia, and Africa
- Potatoes, sweet potatoes, and corn became important parts of people's diets. As a result, people lived longer and populations increased.
- Europeans profited from new trade patterns. They controlled sea routes.
- Europeans and other groups in the Eastern Hemisphere adapted cultural practices from other regions of the world.

PRACTICE

CALIFORNIA CONTENT
STANDARD 7.11.2

The Columbian Exchange

DIRECTIONS: Choose the letter of the *best* answer.

1 Where did the potato originate?

A Europe

B Asia

C Africa

D the Americas

2 What was *one* effect of the global exchange?

A North America became a major exporter of horses.

B The population of Europe increased after 1700.

C The population of Asia decreased after 1700.

D Agriculture in Europe became less diverse.

3 In what way did the Columbian Exchange have an impact on Europe?

A Europeans were helped a little but mostly harmed by the Columbian Exchange.

B Europeans mostly benefited from new trade and the introduction of new crops.

C The Columbian Exchange had very little lasting effect on Europe or the Americas.

D Europeans were introduced to dozens of new plants, animals, and technologies.

4 Which statement summarizes the impact of the Columbian Exchange on the Americas *most* accurately?

A The Columbian Exchange improved life in every way for the Native Americans.

B New crops and animals helped Native Americans, but European diseases took a terrible toll on their civilizations.

C Without the Columbian Exchange, Native American cultures would have declined.

D Neither the trade that resulted from the Columbian Exchange nor the new crops were helpful to the Native Americans.

5 Why is the Columbian Exchange appropriately named?

A It was a result of Columbus's contact with the Americas.

B Columbus made an important impression on the Americas.

C Most ships traveled to and from what is now Colombia.

D Columbus profited greatly from his voyages to the Americas.

Name _____ Date _____

CALIFORNIA CONTENT STANDARD 7.11.3

The European Economy in the 16th and 17th Centuries

SPECIFIC OBJECTIVE: Examine the origins of modern capitalism; the influence of mercantilism and cottage industry; the elements and importance of a market economy in seventeenth-century Europe; the changing international trading and marketing patterns, including their locations on a world map; and the influence of explorers and map makers.

Read the chart to answer questions on the next page.

> The growth of overseas trade and wealth from the colonies brought about major changes in the economy of Europe.

Rise of Capitalism

- Capitalism is an economic system in which private individuals own resources that are used to make a profit that they keep. Under this system of capitalism, many Europeans started profit-making enterprises.
- Many European merchants became wealthy from overseas trade.
- Many Europeans invested in new colonies. They bought shares in companies that started colonies. When the colony started making a profit from trade, the investors made money.
- Merchants put their new wealth into industries in Europe. At the time, the cottage industry was the way most things were manufactured. Merchants gave raw materials to families in the country. These families were paid to make finished products, such as cloth. The merchants then sold the manufactured goods at a profit.

Growth of Mercantilism

- Several European governments adopted a policy known as mercantilism. This policy let the government profit from the new wealth of the colonies.
- The goal of mercantilism was for a nation to gain as much wealth as it could. It could do this by finding precious metals in its colonies. Or, it could gain gold and silver by selling more goods than it bought. For example, the colonies would ship raw materials to the mother country cheaply. The finished goods could be sold to European countries or to the colonies at a high profit.
- By the 18th century, many people were tired of government control of trade. Some economists started to argue that there should be a market economy, one free of government control.

PRACTICE

CALIFORNIA CONTENT
STANDARD 7.11.3

The European Economy in the 16th and 17th Centuries

DIRECTIONS: Choose the letter of the *best* answer.

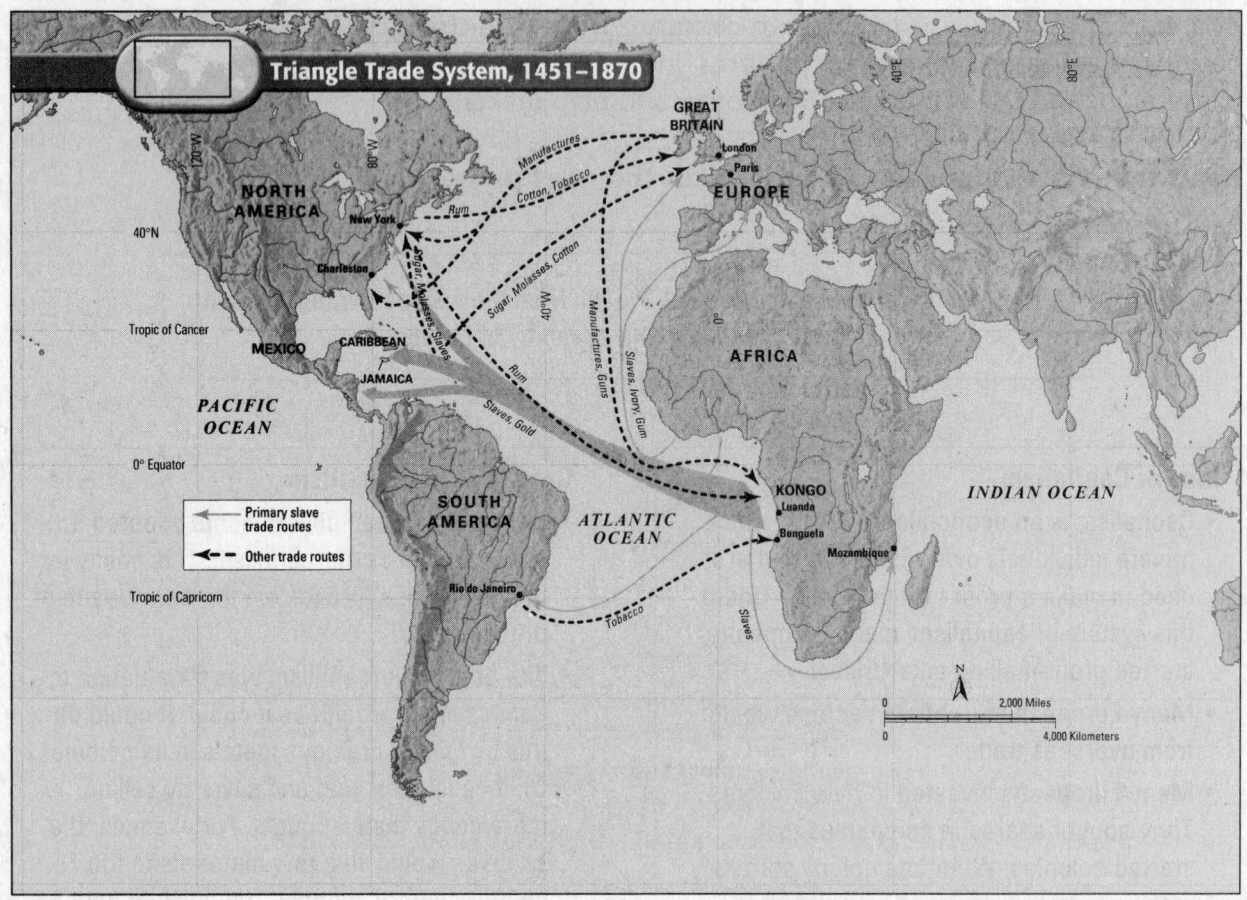

Triangle Trade System, 1451–1870

1 According to the map, the triangle trade routes set up after the 15th century included Europe and

A Africa, North America, and Asia.

B South America, Africa, and Asia.

C Asia, North America, and Africa.

D North America, Africa, and South America.

2 What was *one* effect of the rise of capitalism in Europe?

A a market economy

B stricter tax laws

C fewer manufactured goods

D growth of cottage industries

REVIEW

**CALIFORNIA CONTENT
STANDARD 7.11.4**

The Enlightenment

SPECIFIC OBJECTIVE: Explain how the main ideas of the Enlightenment can be traced back to such movements as the Renaissance, the Reformation, and the Scientific Revolution and to the Greeks, Romans, and Christianity.

Read the chart to answer questions on the next page.

Ancient Greeks and Romans used their powers of reasoning and observation, looking closely at something, to find out more about the world around them. They also stressed the value of individuals.

During the Middle Ages, Christianity was widespread in Europe. Faith was more important than reason. However, Christianity brought the idea of equality in the eyes of God. This became important in the Enlightenment.

The Scientific Revolution brought new ways of thinking about the natural world. Scientists used observation, looking closely at things. They did not accept any idea until it was proven. Philosophers also began to look again at old ideas about government, religion, economics, and education.

The Enlightenment (1700s) was a movement in which thinkers stressed reason and the power of individuals to solve problems. Enlightenment thinking ended many old beliefs.

The Reformation started a trend of questioning authority. By challenging the Catholic Church, reformers showed that people could question even the most powerful institution. This idea helped bring about revolutions later in the Enlightenment.

The Renaissance brought new interest in the classic works of Greece and Rome. Once again, reason and logic were stressed. In addition, humanism focused on what people could do. People were expected to use their minds to solve problems and do great things. New inventions like the printing press helped spread new ideas.

PRACTICE

CALIFORNIA CONTENT
STANDARD 7.11.4

The Enlightenment

DIRECTIONS: Choose the letter of the *best* answer.

1 What was important to Enlightenment thinkers?

   A the past

   B authority

   C faith

   D reason

2 How did the Reformation prepare the way for the Enlightenment?

   A Protestant churches encouraged their followers to believe the truth as stated in the Bible.

   B The Reformation showed that even very powerful institutions could be challenged.

   C Some of the leaders of the Enlightenment gained experience as leaders of the Reformation.

   D The period in which the Reformation occurred led directly into the Enlightenment.

3 How did Christianity influence the Enlightenment?

   A The Enlightenment reinforced Christian values throughout Europe.

   B The pope supported rulers who practiced Enlightenment principles.

   C Christianity urged its followers to question old beliefs and the truth of the Bible.

   D Christianity introduced the idea of equality of all people in the eyes of God.

4 How did Enlightenment thinkers use ideas from the Scientific Revolution?

   A They questioned old beliefs about government, education, and economics.

   B They used reason to argue for stricter government control of people's lives.

   C They experimented with new ways of practicing their religious faith.

   D They turned to nature for solutions to the problems of society.

Name _____   Date _____

CALIFORNIA CONTENT
STANDARD 7.11.5

Influence of Enlightenment Thinkers

SPECIFIC OBJECTIVE: Describe how democratic thought and institutions were influenced by Enlightenment thinkers.

Read the summary to answer questions on the next page.

Enlightenment Thinkers

John Locke's Ideas

Locke believed that people are born free and equal with the right to life, liberty, and property. He also believed that people have the ability to govern themselves and that government is based on the consent of the people. The purpose of the government is to protect people's natural rights. If the government fails to do this, the people have the right to overthrow it.

Baron de Montesquieu's Ideas

Montesquieu believed the powers of government should be separated. One branch should make the laws. One should carry out the laws. One should decide what the laws mean. Each branch limits the others.

Jean Jacques Rousseau's Ideas

Rousseau believed that a direct democracy is the only good type of government. In a direct democracy people make a social contract. They give up some freedom to protect the common good. Like Locke, Rousseau believed that the government gains its power from the people. He believed that all people are equal and that there should be no nobles.

Influence of Enlightenment in America

Enlightenment ideas had a great influence on the American Founders. Thomas Jefferson used Locke's ideas about natural rights in the Declaration of Independence. The colonists based their rebellion against Britain on Locke's idea that people can overthrow the government if it does not protect their rights. Americans also used Enlightenment ideas in the U. S. Constitution:

- Representative government and limiting the power of the government —Locke
- Three branches of government and checks and balances—Montesquieu
- Public election of the president and congress—Rousseau

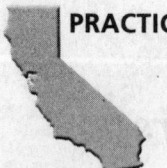

PRACTICE

CALIFORNIA CONTENT
STANDARD 7.11.5

Influence of
Enlightenment Thinkers

DIRECTIONS: Choose the letter of the *best* answer.

1 People's willingness to give up some of their rights in return for protection of others was called

A revolution.

B the scientific method.

C the Bill of Rights.

D a social contract.

2 What was the reason for the colonists' rebellion against the British government?

A England was too far away to be able to govern the colonies well.

B The British government violated their rights.

C The British government was corrupt.

D They wanted more profit from their trade with Britain.

_____
"Power should be a check to power."
_____
                                    —Baron de Montesquieu

3 The idea expressed in the quotation is the basis of

A a constitutional monarchy.

B a system of checks and balances.

C voting by secret ballot.

D representative government.

4 John Locke's ideas about the natural rights of people were incorporated by Thomas Jefferson into the

A Constitution.

B Declaration of Independence.

C Laws of Virginia.

D Articles of Confederation.

5 What resulted from Montesquieu's influence on the Constitution?

A public election

B Bill of Rights

C representative government

D three branches of government

6 Which statement summarizes the *most* important effect of Enlightenment thinkers on later societies?

A Enlightenment thinkers addressed both social and political issues.

B Enlightenment thinkers left behind a body of important texts.

C Enlightenment thinkers influenced development of democratic institutions and thought.

D Enlightenment thinkers proposed some interesting ideas about government.

REVIEW

CALIFORNIA CONTENT STANDARD 7.11.6

Influence of the Magna Carta on Later Documents

SPECIFIC OBJECTIVE: Discuss how the principles in the Magna Carta were embodied in such documents as the English Bill of Rights and the American Declaration of Independence.

Read the summary and chart to answer questions on the next page.

The Magna Carta

King John of England was forced to sign the Magna Carta in 1215. This document was the beginning of democratic government. It gave basic political rights to the nobles. It showed that no one is above the law, including the king.

The document was later seen as safeguarding legal rights for all English citizens. These included the right to a jury trial, protection of the law, and no taxation without representation.

Development of Democratic Ideas

	Trial by jury	No taxation without representation	Protection of the law	Right to petition	Free speech	Natural rights	Religious freedom
Magna Carta (1215)	X	X	X				
English Bill of Rights (1689)	X	X	X	X			
Declaration of Independence (1776)	X	X	X	X	X	X	
U.S. Bill of Rights (1791)	X	X	X	X	X		X

PRACTICE

CALIFORNIA CONTENT
STANDARD 7.11.6

Influence of the Magna Carta on Later Documents

DIRECTIONS: Choose the letter of the *best* answer.

1 The original purpose of the Magna Carta was to

  A change the English court system.

  B decrease the rights of nobles.

  C reform the tax system.

  D limit the power of the king.

2 What was the historical importance of the Magna Carta?

  A It led to revolution.

  B It led to the overthrow of a king.

  C It was the first document signed by a king.

  D It established a foundation for democratic government.

3 Which rights are included in the Magna Carta?

  A trial by jury; right to vote on taxes

  B protection of the law; free speech

  C religious freedom; no taxation

  D right to vote; trial by jury

4 What right does the Magna Carta guarantee that later became part of the Sixth Amendment to the U.S. Constitution?

  A right to trial by jury

  B right to a court-appointed lawyer

  C right to face witnesses

  D right to a speedy trial

Use the chart on page 151 to answer questions 5 and 6.

5 How did the Magna Carta influence later political documents?

  A The Magna Carta set a precedent for guaranteeing basic political rights.

  B Later documents were voted on by the people, not just the nobility.

  C As a result of the Magna Carta, free speech was an important right in all later documents.

  D The idea of natural rights was in the Magna Carta and all later documents.

6 Which pattern is apparent from the chart?

  A Later documents had fewer rights than those included in the Magna Carta.

  B Later documents included only the rights guaranteed in the Magna Carta.

  C Later documents added rights to those guaranteed in the Magna Carta.

  D Later documents included many rights, although not the same ones as in the Magna Carta.

Copyright © McDougal Littell/Houghton Mifflin Company